よりによって　あのソーセージなんかと！
With Sausage Boy, of all people.
UCI
日本は湿度が高くて息がつまる
Japan is so humid, I'm gasping for air.
音もゆがむ……
Warps sound too.
脱出できないなら いっそ音楽なんか やめてしまおうか……
If I can't leave, maybe I should quit music.
ヒク
Twitch

のだめ王国の住人たちを紹介♥
カプリチオーソ　カンタービレ！
———がぼん…!!（意味なし）

Meet the Residents of Nodame-Land!

Cappriccioso cantabile
Golly goo! (Nodame nonsense)

Megumi Noda

Our heroine, known as **Nodame.**
Sophomore, majoring in piano.
A free spirit both in her music and personality.
Fell in love at first sight with Chiaki.

野田恵
～通称・のだめ～（のだめぐみ）
ピアノ科2年。
好き勝手にピアノを弾く、天真爛漫（てんしんらんまん）な不思議ちゃん。千秋せんぱ～いに一目惚（ひとめぼ）れして、ただ今ラブラブ真っ最中♡

Shinichi Chiaki

Junior, majoring in piano.
Father is famous pianist.
Cool heartthrob who actually aspires to be a conductor.

千秋真一（ちあきしんいち）
ピアノ科3年。
有名ピアニストの息子でエリート音大生。でも、本当は指揮者を目指すオレ様な男。のだめに好かれるオトコ前（？）なヤツとは彼のこと！

Saiko Tagaya

Junior, majoring in voice.
Chiaki's ex, whose family owns a famous musical instruments' store.
Is she Nodame's rival?
She still has feelings for Chiaki.

多賀谷彩子（たがやさいこ）
声楽科3年。
有名楽器店のお嬢様。千秋のモト彼女でのだめのライバル（？）。今も千秋のことが好きな感じがプンプンに漂（ただよ）ってます！

のだめカンタービレ
Nodame Cantabile
#1
二ノ宮知子
TOMOKO NINOMIYA

Ryutaro Mine
Sophomore, majoring in violin.
Family owns Uraken, a Chinese
restaurant located behind
the music college.
Rock'n'roller mad about his electric violin
On same wavelength as and best
buddies with Nodame.
峰龍太郎
(みねりゅうたろう)
ヴァイオリン科2年。
大学の裏にある中華料理店「裏軒(うらけん)」の息子。
エレキヴァイオリンを愛用するロッカー青年。のだめ
とは同じニオイがする、いわゆるマブダチってヤツ！
Ryutaro Mine
Masumi Okuyama
Junior, majoring in wind, string instruments and percussion.
Transvestite timpanist who frequently suffers from claustrophobia.
Rivals Nodame in his passion for Chiaki.
奥山真澄(おくやまますみ)
管弦楽科3年。
閉所恐怖症がたまにキズなティンパニー奏者。千秋
を愛するが故(ゆえ)にのだめを勝手にライバル視
する女の子!?　いやいや違う！　ヒゲがチャーム
ポイントの男の子です♥
Masumi Okuyama
Other professors:
Kozo Eto
Loud, strict tutor to the supposedly
most gifted students.
Hajime Tanioka
Tutor specializing in basket cases
and delinquents.
Sebastiano Vieira
World-famous conductor and
Chiaki's idol. Because of Vieira,
Chiaki aspires to be a conductor.
セバスチャーノ・ヴィエラ
千秋がもっとも尊敬する世界
的指揮者。千秋は彼に憧(あ
こが)れて指揮者を目指す！
Sebastiano Vieira
——その他大学の教授——
江藤耕三(えとうこうぞう)
『エリート専門』のハリセン先生。
谷岡肇(たにおかはじめ)
『落ちこぼれ専門』の先生。

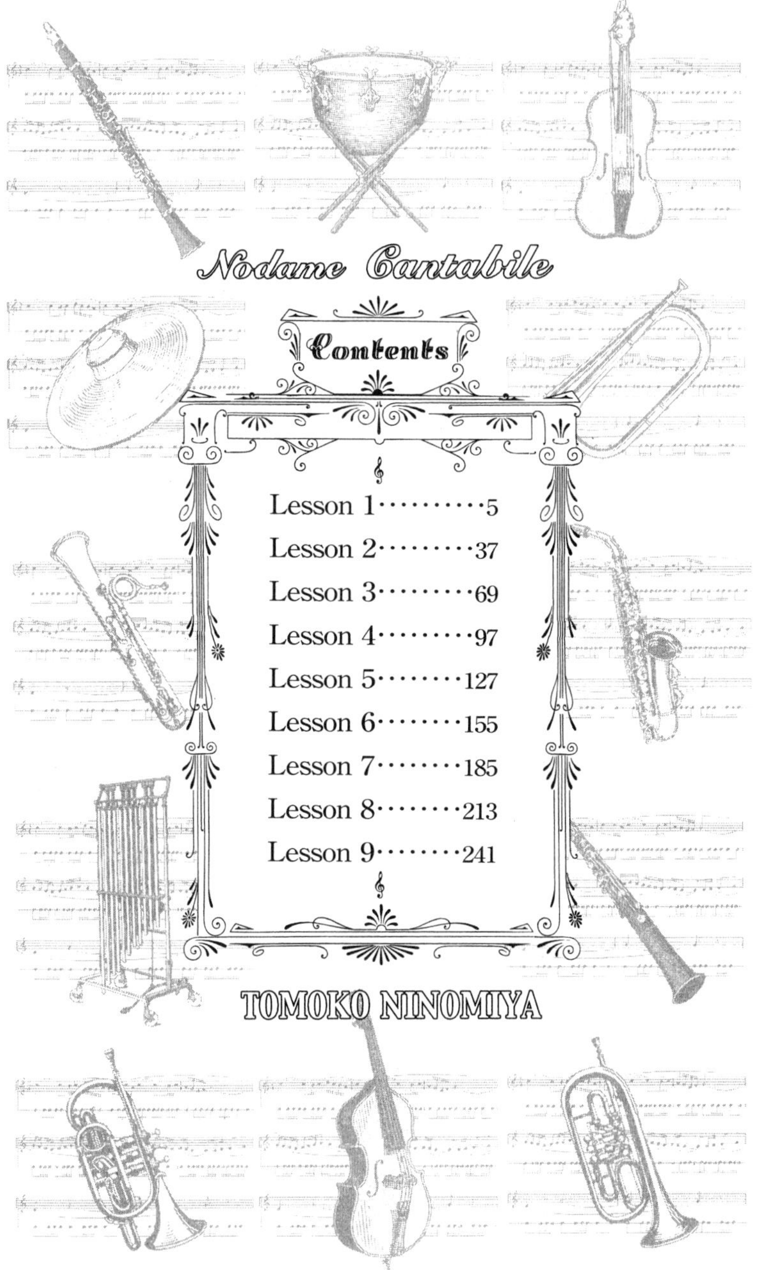

Nodame Cantabile

Contents

TOMOKO NINOMIYA

Lesson 1

My dearest Professor Vieira.
I wanted this year to finally get to see you conduct *Macbeth* at the Vienna State Opera.

親愛なるヴィエラ先生

今年こそ
観に行きたかった

先生が指揮するウィーン
国立オペラ座での《マクベス》

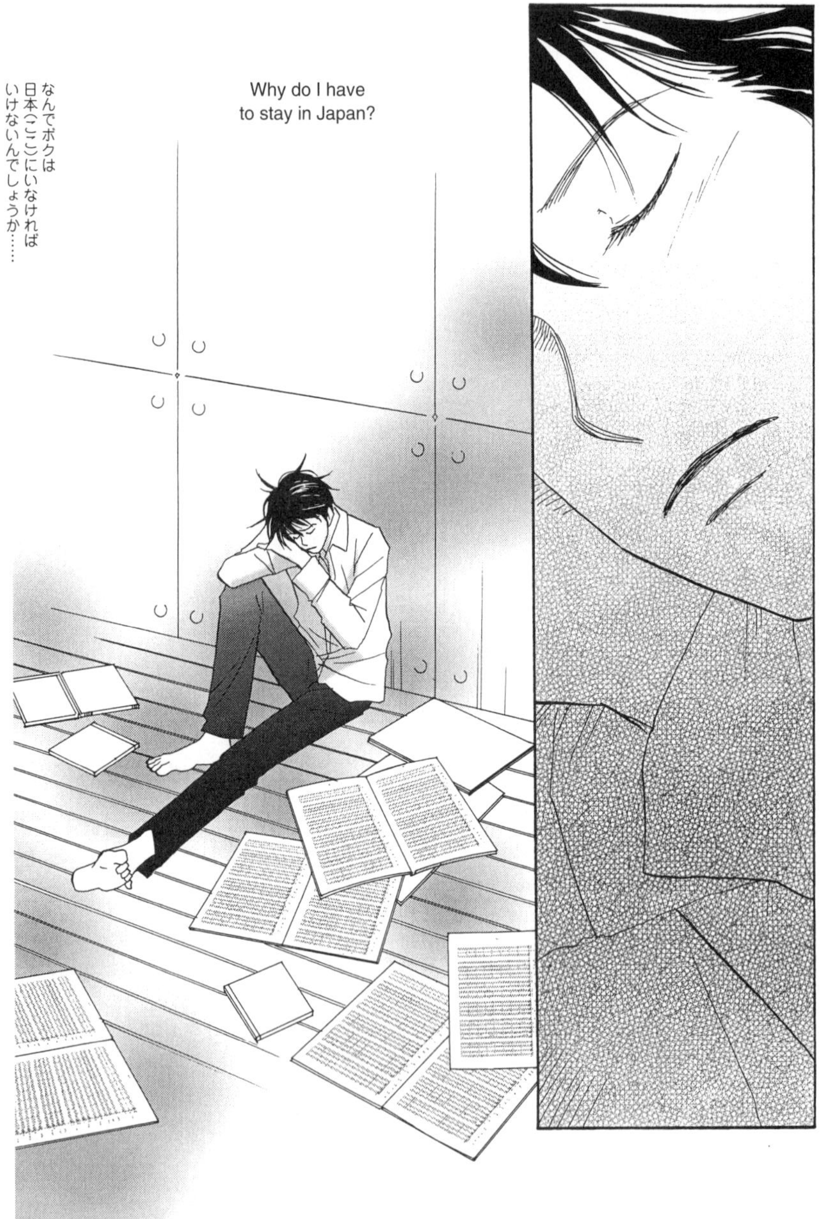
Why do I have
to stay in Japan?

なんでボクは
日本(ここ)にいなければ
いけないんでしょうか……

学校法人桃ヶ丘音楽学園
桃ヶ丘音楽大学大学院
桃ヶ丘音楽大学
Momogaoka College of Music
Graduate Studies
Undergraduate Studies

Dreadful.

へたくそ！

Truly dreadful.

どへたくそ！

みーんな
へたくそ！
They're all hopeless.
オレさま
千秋さま♡
Chiaki's so cool!
キャー♡
今日も怒ってる
Gorgeous! Moody as ever.
へー
あれがうわさの
千秋先輩……
That's the famous Chiaki. I see.
よく
わかんないけど
本当にえらそー
Thinks he's God's gift.
ズカ
ズカ
March, stride
わーっ 見て見て
Look, look!
ピアニストの
千秋雅之（まさゆき）の
息子なんでしょ
Isn't his father Masayuki Chiaki, the famous pianist?
親の七光り系
ってやつ？
Reflected glory?
千秋（ちあき）さまよ！
It's Chiaki!
そんなこと
ないよー
千秋さまは♡
No way!
優秀な生徒しか教えないっていう
カリスマ教師
江藤（えとう）先生の
いちばんのお気に入りなんだしー
He's Prof. Eto's star pupil. Eto's a big personality who only takes the most talented kids.
ピアノ
すっごいうまい
らしーよー
Chiaki is apparently a brilliant pianist.

なんと
わたし 今日は
デパ地下の
限定20食
スペシャル弁…

そのまえに
お昼
お昼！

べつに
いいけど…

ちょっと
聴(き)きに
いかない？

ねえ
これから
レッスンかな？

の……

のだめ――!!

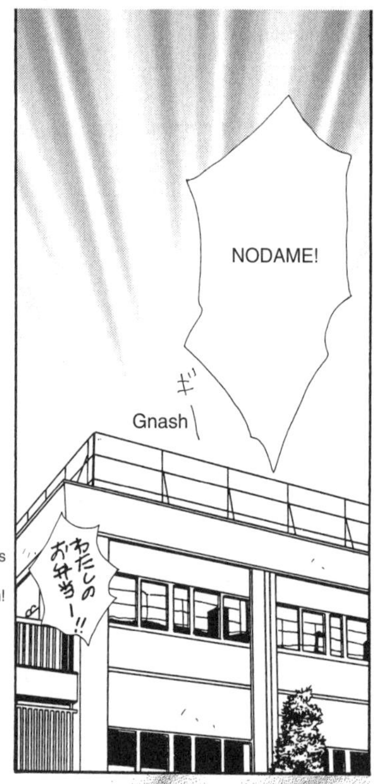
NODAME!
ギ
Gnash
わたしのお弁当ー!!

That's MY lunch!

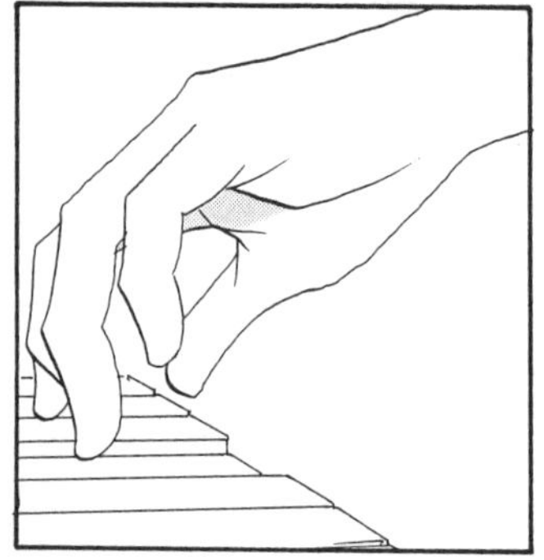

I hear Hayakawa from conducting will study abroad.

指揮科の早川(はやかわ)くん留学するんだってー

ドイツらしいよ

すごーい! どこに?

Wow! Where?
Germany, it seems.

なんであんなソーセージの原料みたいな奴(やつ)が留学!?

Huh, that fat slob! They'll make sausages out of him.

やぁ

Dear me

Export mistake.

「輸出」のまちがいじゃないのか?

Damn!

BANG

くそっ!!

What the hell am I doing?

オレはいったいなにをやってるんだ!?

What do you think you're doing?

なーにやっとんじゃー

BANG

CUT IT OUT!

ゴルア!!

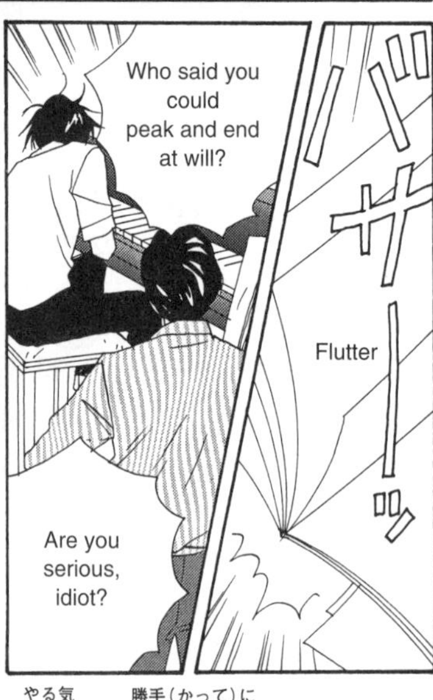

やる気あんのか!? ボケーッ

勝手(かって)に盛り上がって勝手に終わらすな！

おまえを推薦したオレの顔に泥をぬるつもりじゃないやろな

総譜(そうふ)!?
なんやコラ……
ん？
曲かておまえの好きなベートーヴェンやろが
This is Beethoven. You love Beethoven.
ちったぁ気合入れて……
So play with a bit more passion.
Hey!
What's this?
The conductor's score.*
※総譜＝合奏するすべての音部をまとめてある楽譜。指揮者が用いるスコア。
*The conductor's score shows all the instrumental parts.
は……なんでピアノのおまえが総譜なんか持っとんのや？
You're a pianist. Why do you need a conductor's score?
ご丁寧(ていねい)にチェックまで入れて……
You've even got notes.
Chuckle
おまえ指揮者にでもなるつもりか？
You planning on becoming a conductor?
Toss
ふざけんなっ
Dream on.

ピアノもろくに弾けんくせにアホなこと—

うっせーなジジイ

ギャーギャーピーピー

バカのひとつ覚えみてーにf（フォルテ）！f（フォルテ）！

火のように（コンフォーコ）！

借金の取り立てみたいなレッスンしやがって

なにがエリート専門〝江藤塾〟だ！

てめぇの生徒はみんな同じ弾き方すんだよ!!

気持ち悪（わ）りィ

オレの才能に目をつけたんなら余計（よけい）なこと教えんな！

西へ帰れ!! ハリセン教師

言いたいことは
それだけか？
Is that all you have to say?
まだ
言っても
いいのか！
You want me continue?
いやっ
No,
もうええ わかった！
it's OK. I get it.
もう
オレの
レッスンには
来んでええ
You need not come anymore.
選抜学生コンサートもべつの生徒に出てもらう
I'll ask another student to take your place at the invitational.
おまえは
あかん……
You're no good.
オレの
見込みちがい
やった
You've disappointed me.
BEETHOVEN
Adios.
じゃあな
Slam

That's right.

そうだよ

I want to be a conductor.

オレは指揮者になりたいんだ

I've been to concerts worldwide since I was a child

小さいころからピアニストの父に連れられ

with my father, the pianist.

世界中の舞台を見てきた

The magnificent orchestras of Europe.

ヨーロッパの荘厳なオーケストラ

Opera.

オペラ

And...
そして——
the conducting genius of Sebastiano Vieira.
セバスチャーノ・ヴィエラの指揮——

オレはすぐに音楽に夢中になった
Music immediately became my passion.
父の顔を使っては劇場にもぐり込み
My father's connections made it easy for me to slip into the concert halls.
ちがう ちがう！
No, no!
止めて 止めて！
Stop, stop!
ヴィエラ先生のリハもよく観(み)にいった
I often went to Prof. Vieira's rehearsals.
Uaargh
う〜…
右から2番目のバイオリンのチューニング
You, second violinist from the right! Your tuning's all wrong.
オレの代わりに棒ふるか？
Wanna take the baton for a while?
うんっ！
Yessir!
ところで君。どこの子？
Who are you, kid?
Ha, ha, ha
それがきっかけでオレは先生に気に入られ
Vieira took a shine to me.

まだ子供のオレにも先生はいろいろなことを教えてくれた
I was still a kid. But the maestro taught me all sorts of things.
知ってるかー モーツァルトはスカトロ好きだったんだぞーー
You know what? Mozart had a thing for smut.
スカトロ？
Smut?
父と離婚した母と共に日本に帰ることになったオレは——
when my parents got divorced, and I was going back to Japan with my mother...
先生！
Maestro!
ボク 絶対指揮者になるから！
I vow to become a conductor.
だから……大きくなったらボクを先生の弟子にして！
So please take me on as your apprentice when I'm bigger.
そして
And ...
ああ……いつでも待ってるよ
I'll always be here.
きみはわたしの弟子だからな！
'Cos you're my apprentice.
一人でも勉強しておけよー
Study hard on your own.
せんせぇー
M-Maestro!
ボクは絶対指揮者になる！
I know I'll be a conductor.

そして　いつかきっとヨーロッパの最高の楽団(オーケストラ)と

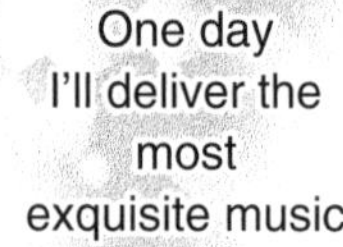

with the best
orchestras in
Europe.

最高の音楽を奏でたい——

Beethoven's Piano Sonata, *Pathetique.*
ベートーヴェンのピアノ・ソナタ〈悲愴(ひそう)〉——
Talk about improvisation!
すっげーデタラメ……
Pathetic is right.
これじゃ〈悲惨(ひさん)〉だ
Wait.
ちがう！
Practically murdering the piece—but it's not wrong.
デタラメだけど間違ってるんじゃない……
Really good, actually.
すごいうまい！
What is this?
なんだこれ……!?

いったい
だれが……

Who is it?

真一(しんいち)!

Shinichi!

Don't
ignore me!

無視しないでヨ!

江藤先生のところクビになったって本当!?

Is it true that
Prof. Eto
kicked you out?

Saiko...

彩子(さいこ)……

江藤先生にあやまって
許してもらいなさいよ！

なんで？

なんでって……
あの先生厳しいけど
うちの学校じゃ
いちばん有能で有名な
先生なのよ

それに　せっかく選抜コンサートにも出られることになってたのに！

いいよ
もう……

オレ　べつに
ピアニストに
なりたいわけじゃないし

だったら
指揮科に
転科しなさいよ

なんで
ピアノ科に
入ったのよ

ピアノの
練習

それに
指揮の勉強は
ちゃんと自分で
やってるし

オレの先生は
ヴィエラ先生
だけだから
Vieira is my only teacher.
余計なこと
教わりたくない
I don't need all this other stuff.
イラ
イラ
Huh! Frown
だったら さっさと
留学すればいいのに
Then hurry up and go study abroad, you fool!
バッカみたい
What an idiot!
飛行機が怖くて
乗れない なんて
To be so afraid
of flying!
1回胴体着陸
経験したからって
なによ!?
OK, so you were once in a crash-landing.
無キズ
だったくせに
It's not as if you were injured.
かんたんに
言うなぁ!!
Easy for you to say!
ドンッ
Pound
泣き叫ぶ
乗客
The screaming, crying passengers.
わああ
Aaargh!
おろせ おろせ
Get me off! Get me off!
真一大丈夫よ
It's OK, Shinichi.
死ぬっ
I'll die
死イイイ
I'll die
真一おちついて
Calm down, Shinichi.
死の恐怖……
The terror of impending death...

じゃあ
船で行けば
いいじゃない
Then go
by sea!
船だって
同じだ！
A ship is
just as bad.
えっ？　なんで？
Why?
体験してないおまえになにがわかる⁉
You didn't go
through it.
What do you
know?
ブル
ブル
Tremble, shake
海は宇宙と
いっしょだ……
The sea is
like space.
空気も
ない
No air.
孤独の暗闇……
Alone in
the dark...
人類は月へは行けても
まだ海の　いちばん深い場所へは
行ったことがないんだぞ
Humans have
been to the moon.
But they still haven't
been to the deepest,
darkest places of
the sea.
ようするに
溺(おぼ)れたことが
あるのね真一……
I see. You
almost
drowned,
Shinichi...
ガタ
ガタ
Shudder, shiver
オレ……
Maybe...
もう音楽
やめようかな
I'll quit
music.

What?

え？

Even if I turn pro in Japan,

いくら日本でプロになってがんばったところで

it's pointless if I can't perform in Europe.

ヨーロッパで演奏できなきゃ意味ないし

Maybe I'll get a job in your family business,

おまえン家(ち)の会社……

Tagaya Musical Instruments.

多賀谷（たがや）楽器の社員にでもしてもらおーかな

Don't go.

帰るなよ

Stay with me today.

今日……

やめてよ
Stop that.
わたしたち もう そーゆー関係じゃ ないんだから
We're not together anymore.
それに
Anyway
わたし 負け犬 なんかキライ！
I don't go for losers!
犬…
Loser...
あんたなんか どこ行ったって いっしょよ！
You'd be the same anywhere!

♬フーン
Doo-uppa-doo,
SWEET HOUSE
dooby-
dooby-doo
♬フン ♬フン
♬フーン フンフン
Doo-uppa-doo
プリプリ マート
Puripuri-mart
Doo-da-dog-doo
ネコのフ〜ン♬

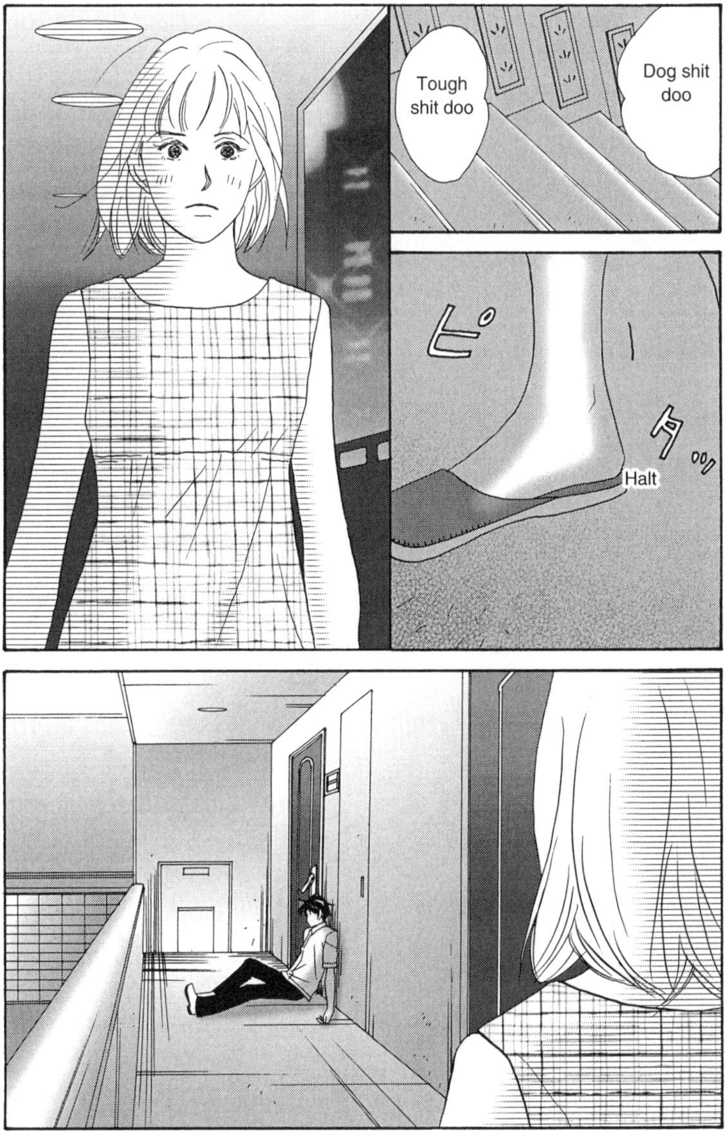

かたい♬

♬フーン
フーン

Dog shit doo

Tough shit doo

ピ

タッ

Halt

なんとか
先輩……

ぴぎっ

Snore

Um, what was your name?

なんだっけ？

What was it?

Eeek!

フー
Breathe
ピクン…
Twitch
風――
The wind.
風の音がする
I can hear the wind.

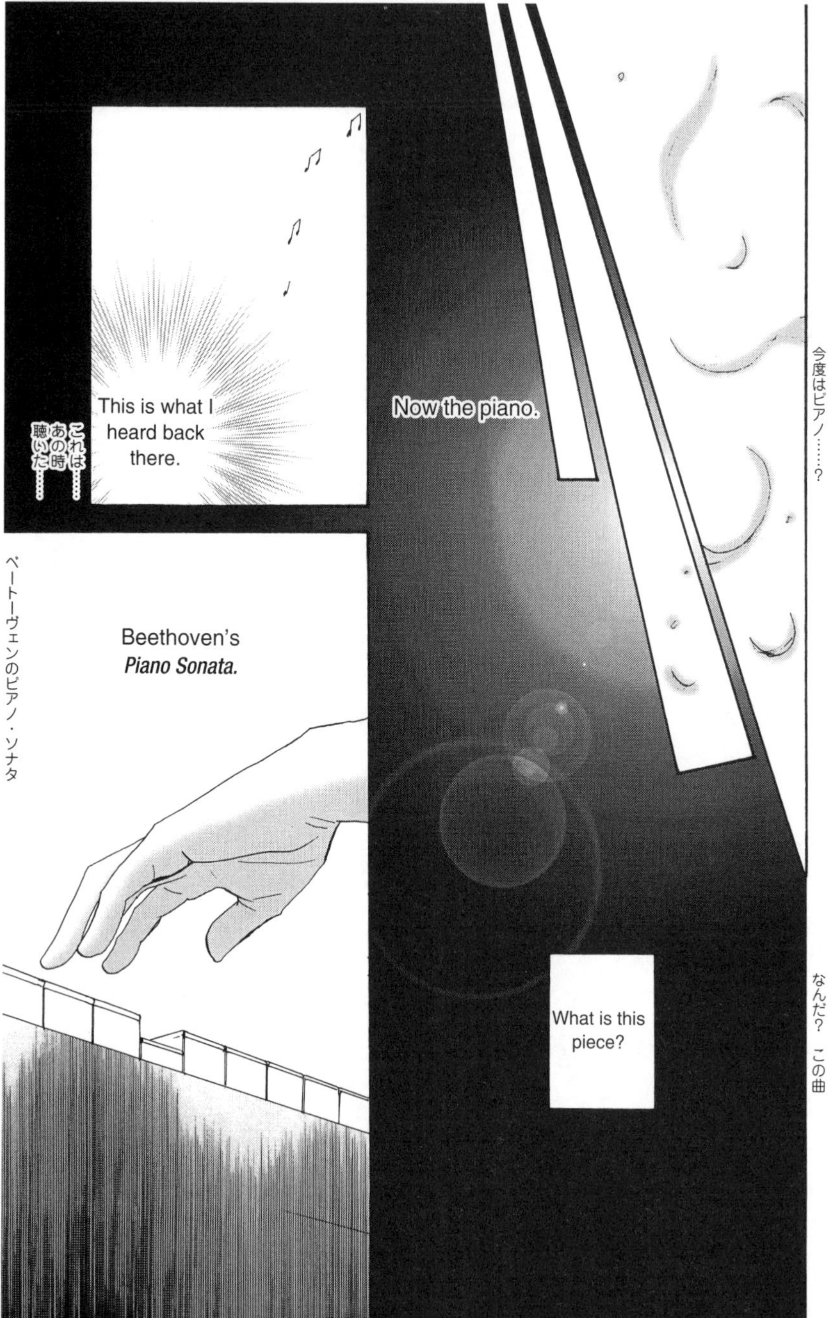
今度はピアノ……？
Now the piano.
なんだ？ この曲
What is this piece?
これは あの時 聴いた……
This is what I heard back there.
ベートーヴェンのピアノ・ソナタ
Beethoven's *Piano Sonata.*

Egg ramen

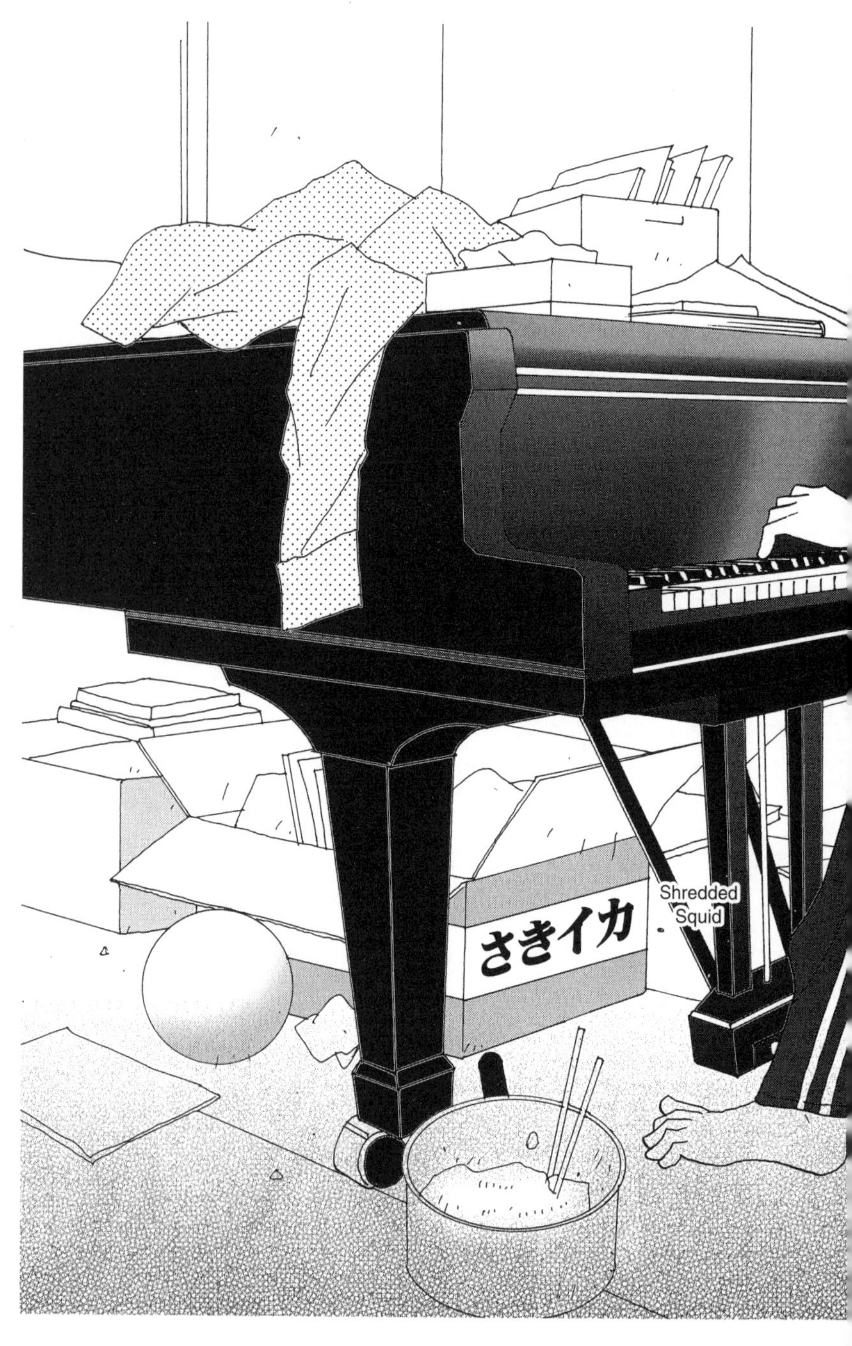
さきイカ
Shredded Squid

ゴミの中で
美しく響く
ピアノ・ソナタ
Resonating amid the rubbish was this exquisite piano sonata,
カプリチオーソ(気ままに気まぐれに)カンタービレ(歌うように)
Capriccioso cantabile. Lively and free, smooth and lyrical.
Shredded Squid
これがオレと野田恵(のだめぐみ)との出会いだった
This marked my first encounter with Megumi Noda.

Lesson 2

NODAME CANTABILE

ここはどこ？
Where am I?
あれはだれ？
Who is that?
さきイカ
Shredded Squid
クラ
Sway
Clank

ぶわっ
Swarm
!?
ブーン
ブーン
Bzzz, bzzz
Eureka!
ひいいいー!!
ピタッ
Halt
I remem-ber.
思い出した!
Shinichi Chiaki!
千秋先輩!
Remember what happened yesterday?
昨日のこと
覚えてましゅか～?
うきゅっきゅ～♥
Ooh!
Clank

Dash
Oh!
あっ
Please!
先輩！
Slam
I'm
in the hallway of my building.
ここは　オレのマンション!?
202
千秋
202
Chiaki
She lives
オレの……
next door.
となりの部屋——!?

ふぁ…
Float
!?
わあぁ——っ!!
Yuck!
ほこりっ
Dust
What's wrong with that woman?
なんなんだ!? あの女
ザァァ…
Gush
千秋先輩!
Shinichi Chiaki!
ギャフ
Hiya!
Chiaki had a vision of her rising up from the trash.
↖こう見えた
She goes to the same music school as me?
あれはうちの音大の生徒なのか!?
ゴミ
Trash
あ、、、あんなのが
同じ大学で
同じマンションで
となりの部屋!?
I don't believe such a nutcase goes to the same school
and, furthermore, lives next door!
Remember what happened yesterday?
"昨日のこと覚えてましゅか〜?"
ひっ
Flinch

Like hell I remember!

覚えてねぇ!!

Chiaki!

千秋せんぱ～いっ

ぶほっ

Splutter

Eeek!

げっ

Nodame?

のだめ？

Your belit!
ベルト〜〜〜!!
You left it at my place yesterday.
昨日うちに忘れていったですよー♡
ビシィ
Straighten
おぉ〜
Wow!
ひゃ
Yikes!
I-It's not mine.
That belt's not mine.
Hangover
二日酔い
あれは先輩だヨ〜
オ……オレのじゃねえ!
そんなベルト……
ない!
Of course it's yours! I should know—I undid it.
先輩のだよ わたしがはずしたから覚えてるよ
Y-You've got me
mixed up with someone else.
人ちがいだ! それはオレじゃない!
だっ
Rush
Now don't be silly.
I remember that butterfly birthmark on your neck.
ホラ 首に蝶(ちょう)の形のアザがあるぅー
No such thing!
I swear it.
断じてない!
でもニオイが同じだョ〜
But I recognize your smell!
ついてくるなぁ
Leave me alone!

のだめ……
Nodame...
どーゆーこと!?
What's going on?
千秋様とっ
With Chiaki
昨日拾ったんだ♡
Yesterday I picked up
千秋先輩
the most adorable Chiaki.
なんで!?
How?
どこで!?
Where?
取り調べ
Interrogation
うちの前で……
In front of my apartment.
なんでだかよくわかんないけど
I don't know why.
ぷぷっ……
Tee-hee!
先輩の寝言っておもしろいんだよ――
He says the funniest things in his sleep.
"逃げろ!"とか
Like, "Escape"
"助けてクレー"とか
and "Help"
富士山が爆発しちゃったらしくてー
He was dreaming that Mt. Fuji had exploded.
アハハハ
Ha-ha-ha-ha!

PIANO: change of instructor

ピアノ　担当者変更

Name 氏名	New instructor 新担当者	Notes 備考
Shinichi Chiaki 千秋　真一	Kozo Eto → Hajime Tanioka 江藤耕造 → 谷岡　肇	

谷岡肇（たにおかはじめ）……

知らない先生だな

Prof. Tanioka?

谷岡先生？

He usually teaches in room 282.

Thanks.

レッスン中なら　いつも282の部屋にいるよ　サンキュー

Wow!

おー

First time Chiaki's ever thanked me.

千秋にはじめて礼をいわれたー

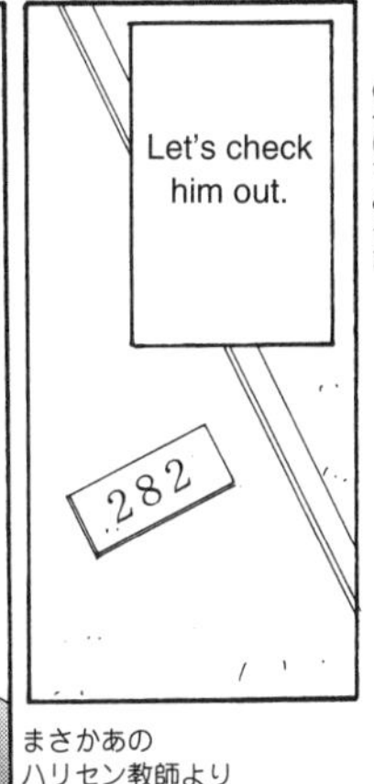

レッスンの様子でものぞいてみるか

まさかあのハリセン教師よりヒドイってことはないだろうが

Gimme five
ヘイ！
Five!
ヘイ！
Fart!
ブーーー！
Ha, ha, ha!
わははは!!
Great as a side show, don't you think?
ね！先生 お遊戯にはピッタリでしょ
Priceless, priceless.
いいよ！いいよ！
Ha-ha-ha!
I like the ending.
最後がいいね〜
おなら体操！
it's called fart-obics

でも「ヘイ！ヘイ！」はあんまりかっこよくないなぁ〜〜〜

そうかにゃー「屁(へ)イ！」って気持ちをこめたんだけど

それはちょっとひねりすぎだし下品だよ〜〜〜

「みんなの歌」も狙(ねら)うんだろ？

ちがうよー先生「ママといっしょ」だよー！

じゃあもう一回！通してやってみよう

はいっ

♬元気に出そう

♬いい音出そう

これが今度のオレの担任教師……？

ドレミファ♬プップップー

ぎゃははははは!!

すげー
笑い声

ギャハハハ
Guffaw
ヒー
Tee-hee-hee
You can hear them a mile off.
あー
Must be Prof. Tanioka.
谷岡先生だろー

あの人の生徒って みんな困った奴(やつ)らしいぜー
I've heard all his students are tricky.
そういえばあの先生
Yeah, he's called the Don of Basket Cases.
うわさじゃ“落ちこぼれ専”教師って言われてるもんなー

オレが……
I'm a..
落ちこぼれ!?
basket case?

Drinks' party?
え〜〜〜
合コン?

悪いけど わたし パス！
I'll pass, thanks.
なんで？
Why?
ええー
What!
今日は素子(もとこ)のいとこのT大の人たちよ
Motoko's cousin is coming with some of his T University friends.
下品な合コンじゃないわよー
Not one of those tacky parties.
彩子 千秋くんとは別れたんでしょう!?
You split up with Chiaki, didn't you?
テストがあるし のどの調子を整えたいのよ
I've got an exam tomorrow. I want to get my voice in shape.
真一なんて関係ないの！
Nothing to do with Shinichi.
彩子はえらいなー
You're so admirable, Saiko.
オペ研※でもいちばんのソプラノだもんねー
You're the top soprano in the Opera Club too.
※オペ研＝オペラ研究会
あっ
Oh!
じゃあ わたし ここで！
I have to go.
え
What?
またね！
See you!
あら〜〜……
Oh my!
そういうことだったのね〜……
I see.
いつの間に…
When did that happen?
わぁ
Goodness!

あれって指揮科の早川くんじゃない!?
That's Hayakawa from conducting, isn't it?
えっ そうなの？
Really?
彼 来年ドイツに留学するっていう人よね？
The one who's going to study in Germany next year.
将来有望なんだー
へー
Aha! A promising future.
彩子 そういう人好きね~~~
Right up Saiko's alley.
まぁ そういう意味じゃ 千秋くんと別れたの納得いくわね
Makes sense she split with Chiaki.
落ち目だもんね
His star
is on the wane.
千秋くん
学生選抜も落とされちゃったみたいだしー
He's been dropped from the invitational.
江藤先生にも捨てられちゃったらしいわよー
Prof. Eto seems to have dumped him too.

SWEET HOUSE
ガシャーン
SMASH!
CHOPIN
ピアノ曲集
J.S.BACH
I DUMPED ETO!
江藤（ハリセン）を捨てたのはオレのほうだ!!
Damn.
くそ！
Damn you, Saiko.
彩子の
やつ!!

今のうちに
この忌(い)まわしい
物体を家(うち)から
排除しなくては！

I must remove this hateful object.
ズルズル
Drag-drag

これであいつらも　こたつごと　のだめの部屋へ移るだろう　ゴミはゴミ箱に帰るがいい！

ガチャン
Lock

The *kotatsu* will surely lure them to Nodame's place.

Rubbish should go back to the rubbish bin.

ガチャガチャ
ガチャン
Click-clickety-click

What!

え!?

ひィ
Eeek!

Owooo, I am a gho-ost!

わはは
Ha-ha-ha!
なー！カギ持って出てよかっただろーー
Good thing I took the key.
My, my
まぁー
本当だわーー
Exactly.
ヒドイ男ですネ
How could you?
さーーてこたつこたつ！
Come here, *kotatsu.*
よいしょー
Oopsy-daisy
元にもどしてしきり直しだー
Let's put it back where it was and start again.
もうすぐ除夜の鐘ですヨ〜〜〜♡
The New Year's bell will chime soon.
ゴーン
CHIME
そしてーー
And so it came to pass...
あけましておめでとうーー!!
Happy New Year!
おめでとーー♡
Cheers!

このこたつ祭りは
三箇日中(さんがにちじゅう)
催され

The *kotatsu* festival lasted for 3 whole days.
Beethoven's 9th
第九〜
Bye for now!
じゃあねー
See ya!
またなー
By the end,
my place looked like Nodame's. A living hell.
Oh, hello
I would like to arrange a pickup for large rubbish.

気がつけば

うちは のだめの部屋と化していた

それはこの世の
生き地獄

もしもし 粗大ゴミの回収お願いしたいんですが

Just off to do a bit of shopping.
ちょっとお買い物いってきマス♥
鬼(のだめ)の居(い)ぬ間(ま)に
While the cat's away...
粗大ゴミ
Large Rubbish
粗大ゴミ
Large Rubbish
さらば こたつ
Farewell, *kotatsu.*
もう二度と入ることもあるまい
I'll never use one again.

のだめ
カンタービレ
Nodame
Cantabile
うで組んだ…
うで組んだ…
うで組んだ
Arm-in-arm!
Arm-in-arm!
Arm-in-arm!

NODAME CANTABILE

あの女の
部屋から
異臭が？
となり!?
Is this revolting smell coming from that woman's place?
Next door?
なんだ!?
この臭(にお)いはっ
ぼへっ
Uurrh!
What's this smell?
Pfoar
!!
What on earth is this?
なんじゃ　こりゃー——!!

Yikes!
ひぃ
汁 Foul liquid
アリ
Ants
201
野田☆
201
NODA
ピンポン
ピンポン
ピンポン
ピンポーン
Ding-dong
Ding-dong
Ding-dong
Ding-dong
Yes, hi!
ガン
Smash

はーい!

ぴぎゃ！
千秋先輩っ
Gosh, Chiaki!
開けるか？
フツー……
いきなり
Ow, what kind of nutcase flings open the door without warning?
どうしたん
ですか〜〜
What's up?
あっ わかった！
Oh, I get it.
ベルト取りに
きたんでショ！
You've come to get this belt.
これっ
どけ！
Stand aside.
り？
Eh?
Stomp, stride
先輩!?
Chiaki!
Seaweed
KINOPIO
ASS-TROLOGY 2001
Are you light-assed?

これが同じマンション？
先輩……？
Chiaki...
Are we really in the same building?
掃除！
え？
Time to get cleaning.
Excuse me?
Vacuum cleaner, dustpan—bring out all your cleaning tools.
さきイカ
Shredded Squid
さきイカ
Shredded Squid
BEETHOVEN
掃除道具全部出せ！

掃除道具……
Cleaning tools?
掃除機なら
ベッドの上に
The vacuum cleaner is on the bed.
なんで
ベッドの上に!?
What on earth is it doing there?
ベッドはどこだ!?
Where's the bed?
くそ!
Jesus!
なんだ このゴミの山はっ
What is this pile of rubbish?
オレが全部
撤去してやる!
I'll get rid of it.
シティページ
City Pages
TMG trash bag
あっダメ!
先輩
No, no!
その
段ボールは
Not that box.
必要なものが
たくさん入って
るんです!!
Lots of important things are in it.
ガッコの
道具とか
Like school stuff.

あっ！
その段ボールも
捨てちゃダメッ
No, don't throw that box away.
それには
大事なモノが
入れてあるんです！
It contains my precious things.
コミック
ポンポン
Comic Ponpon
コミック
ポンポン
Comic Ponpon
その段ボールは
宝物入れです！
That box is my treasure chest.
ふざけんな——!!
YOU'VE GOTTA BE JOKING!
うこん
埼玉JACH
Ukon Saitama JACH
やせる
石ケン
Slimming soap
ぶぎゃ——っ
Aaargh!
おい……
コラァ
What's this?

これは なんだ!?
What is it?
それは
I think
たぶん クリーム シチューですっ
that's white sauce stew.
クリーム シチューは 黒いのか!?
Does white sauce stew turn black?
いえっ
Um, no.
とぐろを巻くのか!?
And produce these coiled scraps?
はいっ 1年もたつと……
Well, it's been about a year.
このイクラは なんだ!?
What's happened to this salmon roe?
ごはん です——
Actually, it's rice.
ふぎゃーっ ブラジャー!
Yikes! My bra!
このキノコはっ!?
And these mush-rooms?
洗濯物 ですっ
From my laundry.
はぎゃーっ パンツ!
Eeek! Under-pants!
これは?
What's this?
わかりません!
Dunno.
甲子園の土ー!
Soil from Koshien Stadium!

だまってろ!!
Shut up! 
やっと出たそうじ機
At last the vacuum cleaner
はたはた
Flutter, flutter
ザー
Gush, splash
オレはバカだ……
I'm a fool.

つい
ヤケになって
人の部屋を
掃除して
しまうなんて

ピアノ……
なんだ？
オリジナルの曲か——

What's that you're playing?
なんの曲だ？ それ
Tee-hee
あは
The cleaning song.
掃除の曲♡
"Prelude in Love Major" for you and me.
先輩とわたしの恋の序曲（プレリュード）♡
I see. Improvisation.
即興か……
Piano sonata: "Squeaky Clean."
ピアノ・ソナタ〈清掃〉——
Want to be sucked away?
吸い取られたいか？
You just...
ごら……
play it again.
もう一回弾いてみろ！

今の曲をもう一度――

That same piece.

本当はずっと気になってたんだ

I realized I'd been very aware of her talent.

えへっ

Really?

じゃあもいっかい♡

OK, one more time.

こいつのピアノ――

Her piano.

やっぱり
I knew it.
うまい！
She's good.
手がでかい！
Big hands
難しいことを難なくやってる
that handle difficult tasks with ease.
あ！
Hey!
そこ ちがう！
That bit's wrong.
さっきと同じように弾いて！
Play it the way you played before.
えっ
What?
Eeek!

あわわ
Oh, my!
さっきって……どう弾いたっけ!?
Um, how did I play it before?
こうだろ！
Like this.
あっ　そか！
Oh,
I see.
作り方がでたらめすぎるんだよ！
You’re just playing any way you want.
でも　おもしろい！
Interesting, though.
そう　次
OK,
next bit.
流して——
f（フォルテ）！
Forte.
もう一回！
Again.
……
カンタービレ（歌うように）！
Cantabile.

すご……!

はー……
Oh...

すごいねー先輩
You're amazing, Chiaki.
ちょっと聞いただけで曲覚えちゃって
You've already memorized the piece.
だひ
Aaar-zonked
ポ
Pling
I, on the other hand, am completely exhausted.
のだめクタクター

でも
But
I had so much fun.
楽しかったねー♡

楽しい……
Fun...

ゴミがないと 音が全然ちがうんだねー
The sound is completely different without the rubbish.
あはは
Ha, ha, ha!

Lesson 3

連弾!?

うん

やってみない?

彼女——野田恵くんと千秋くんとで ピアノ2台の連弾レッスン

な

なんでオレが
こんなのと
いっしょにレッスン!?

Why a lesson with this nutcase?

こんなの?

This nutcase?

連弾やるなら
先生とでしょう!?

The only person I should be doing duets with is you, prof.

じょうだんじゃねえ!

You must be joking.

いやー　君と野田くんの
「恋の序曲(プレリュード)」の話を
聞かせてもらってね

Miss Noda told me about your "Prelude in Love Major."

ハハハ

Guffaw

そんな曲は
ありません!

There's no such piece!

君たちの連弾
かなりおもしろそう
だと思うんだよー

I'm sure a duet would be interesting.

野田くんも実は、ピアノうまいしー

Miss Noda is actually a good pianist.

のだめ
こっちの
ピアノー♥

I'll have this piano.

わかってンのか!

See my point?

いくらうまくても
あんなメチャクチャな弾き方する奴に
合わせられるわけないでしょう!!

That may be so, but nobody can duet with someone who plays so recklessly.

君なら
できるよ〜〜

If anyone can do it, it's you.

この大学でいちばん
ピアノうまいし

You're the best pianist here.

ぴくっ

Twitch

それに
指導力!

Good leadership too.

即興でも
野田くんに
1曲ちゃんと
弾かせたなんて
すごいよー

OK, she improvised. But nobody else has been able to get her to play an entire piece.

はい！ 先輩は恋の魔術師ですっ♡
Yes, Chiaki is the Magician of Love.
まあ 後輩指導だと思って——
Think of it as helping an underclassman.
Guffaw
ね♡
OK?
ウキー
Goody!
けいれい…
Salute
後輩指導……
Helping an under-class-man...
曲はモーツァルトの「2台のピアノのためのソナタ」ニ長調
The piece is: Mozart's *Sonata for 2 Pianos in D Major.*
MOZART
うぎっ
Yikes!
知らナイ……
I don't know it.
オレも知らん……
I don't know it either.
けっこー速い曲で合わすの大変だと思うけど
It's quite a fast piece, and I imagine you'll find it hard to keep together.
Ha-ha-ha!
まあ気長に練習してよ
Practice makes perfect but so does patience.
MOZART
冗談だろ！
This has to be a joke.
おい！ 一回読譜したら とっととやるぞ ゴミ女！
OK, you've read the score, now let's get on with it.
Miss Rubbish Dump,
←気短
Impatient

野田恵！

Megumi Noda!

"のだめ"って呼んでくだサイ

Please call me Nodame.

じゃあ おまえがピアノ2で オレが1ね

You're piano 2, I'm 1. OK?

練習したくば5分でしろー

If you need to practice, you've got just 5 minutes.

千秋くん……この曲8分弱あるよ

Er, Chiaki, this piece is just under 8 minutes long.

じゃあ8分弱でしろー

OK. You've got just under 8 minutes.

発奮!!

I'm gonna run the (8分) 8-minute mile!

MOZART

ブブーーッ‥（時間切れ）

Beep (time's up)

テンポは最初 ゆっくりめでいいから

You can keep the tempo slow at the start.

これくらいで トン・トン・トン♪

Like this. Pom-pom-pom

いくぞ！

Here we go.

冒頭は2台のピアノの3オクターブにわたるユニゾンの……

It begins with two pianos playing in unison across three octaves.

バチーン!

Twang

たった2小節で間違えるな——!!
Don't mess up after just two notes!
ぴぎゃ——っ
Eeek!

これは
付点休符！
Look at this note!
Get your basics right!
ンなもの
間違えんな！
Again.
もう１回！
なぜ……
Why?
Why does she play so recklessly?
どうして
こんなメチャクチャに？
チラッ
Glance

YOU'RE NOT EVEN LOOKING AT THE FUCKING SCORE!
楽譜見てねーじゃねーか!!
Aaargh!
ぎゃひ——っ
But I've memorized it.
でもっ ちゃんと暗譜してマス!
Memorized? How?
どこがちゃんとだ!
How does tick-a-tack tick-a-tack tick-a-tack become
♬タカタ♬タカタ♬タカタが
tra-la-la la-la-la-la?
♬タララ♬ラララ ラ～ってどーゆーことだ!?
Um...
な……
somehow.
なんとなく——
Miss Noda has a good ear.
野田くんは耳がいいからー
So she usually learns aurally.
耳で聴いて覚えること多くて——

楽譜見ながら
弾く習慣が
ないんだよね

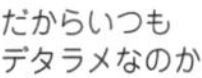

まあ
気長に——ね

じょうだんじゃねえ!

ま……

まにあってます!

掃除じゃねえ！
練習だ！
I haven't come to clean your apartment.
Practice, girl, practice!
Creak, wrench
やんっ
Down boy!
こ…恋の練習（レッスン）ABCはまた今度！
We can practice the abc's of love another time.
縁起でもないこと言うな！
For heaven's sake, cut it out!
なにがやんっだ!!
"Down boy" yourself.
March, stride
オレはピアノの……
I'm here for piano prac...
Oh my God!
Shredded Squid
Shredded Squid

あれから一週間しか
たってないのに……

It's only been a week.
ピザWW
Pizza WW
どうしてここまで……
How could she make such a mess?
S-
ご…… ごめんなさい
Sorry.
I haven't finished memorizing the score.
わたしまだ 暗譜しきれて なくて……
But I promise I will.
でも なんとか 覚えますから
Give me another week. Please... wait.
まって

だから
あと一週間……

一週間も
待てるか!
How can I wait a week?
ザーッ
There
ベビースター→
オレが弾いて
みせるから
I'll play it.
ちゃんと
楽譜見て
聴いてろ!
So keep your eyes on the score while you listen.
どうしても
楽譜見ながら
弾けないなら
If you really can't read the score while you play,
自慢の耳で覚えきれ!
use your formidable aural memory to learn the whole thing properly.
「2台のピアノの
ためのソナタ」
Sonata for 2 Pianos:
SONATE
I
K.V.448
Allegro con spirito
It is said that Mozart wrote this jolly piece to play as a duet at parties with the plump young daughter of a friend.
モーツァルトが
ピアノのうまいデブ娘(知人の子)
との合奏用に作った
あっかるいサロン向き音楽

谷岡先生も
人が悪いな
Prof. Tanioka has a warped sense of humor.
連弾だったら
リストとかブラームスとか
もっとメジャーで
やりやすい定番曲もあるのに
He could have picked something more mainstream like Liszt or Brahms.
くっ……
Uurgh
これは合わせるの大変だぞ！
This one's a nightmare for the pianists to keep together.
うおー
パチ
パチ
パチ
Clap, clap, clap!
Wow!
すごい　すごいー！
うまい～♡
Wow! Brilliant!
先輩のピアノって
正確なんだね～
You play with such precision.
本当に楽譜通りだったヨ～
You played exactly the way it is on the score.

おまえがデタラメすぎるんだよ！
オレは指揮者志望だからな
I plan to be a conductor.
You play like a lunatic.
許せん
Unforgivable!
作曲者の意思は絶対だ！
You must respect the intent of the composer.
オレとやる以上まずはキッチリ弾いてもらうからな！
Keep this in mind when you play with me. Don't cut corners.
ギャヒー
Eeek!
ちがう！
NO!
そこからはピアノ1と入れ替わる！
That's where you give way to piano 1.
「なんとなく」弾くな
Don't just do it any old way.
はっはいー
R-Right.
そこは間を開けて
Pause there.
伴奏小さく！
Keep it small.
テンポ！
Tempo!

学校 School
リットかけて
Give it some *ritardando*, you know, gradually slow down.
オレの音もちゃんと聴けー
Listen to my piano too!
はいっ
Yessir!
そのカオやめろ!!
Don't grimace like that!
えっ
What?
自覚なし
Clueless
まだ全然合ってねえ!
We're not keeping together at all!
それでもミスは減ってきた
Still, she's making fewer mistakes.

勝手に
転調するな──！
don't change the tempo on a whim!
But
でも
I'm getting
なんだか
BANG!
really mad.
ものすごくムカムカしてきた
201
201 NODA
SWEET H
は ─
Sigh
Although I don't think I'm speak-ing out of order.
間違ったことを
言ってるわけじゃ
ないはずなのに

どうしたの？ 先輩……
What's up?
変……
Wrong...
どこですか〜？
Where?
せっかくつっかえずに最後まで弾けたのに
You got to the end without fluffing.
あっ
What?
なんかまた変だった？
Was something else wrong?
のだめ全然わかんなかった〜
I didn't notice at all.
くさい……
Stinks.
え？
Excuse me?
おまえのあたま くさい
Your hair stinks.
えーっ そうですか？
O-Oh, does it?
4日前にちゃんと洗ったのにー
I did wash it 4 days ago.
4日前!?
4 days ago?
くんくん
Sniff, sniff
ひっ
Jesus!
おフロは1日おき
I take a bath every other day,
シャンプーは5日おき
and wash my hair every 5 days.

Tee-hee! Looks can lie. I'm quite a cleanliness freak.
ふふ こう見えても 結構キレイ好きでショ♡
Gush
He-elp!
きゃあああ――っ
No, in your case, what you see is what you get.
見たまんまじゃねーか！
Gush
How on earth
どういう教育を
Gold Shampoo
Plonk
Yikes!
Scrub, scrub
were you brought up?
Sto-op!
受けてきたんだ!!

なにやってんだ　オレは……
And what on earth am I doing?
ブォォ
Blow
どうしてストレスがたまると　こーゆー　わけのわからんボランティアを……
Why do I add to stress by taking on weird charity cases like this?
ファー
A-Ah...
ゴォー
Blow
きもちイ～～
That feels so good.
なんか今わたし
Right now,
こんな気分です～～♡
I feel like this.
ココナッツ島
Coconut Island
王室
Her Royal Highness

オレは
Well, I feel
like this.
こんな気分だ
Blow
トリマー
A dog groomer.

え〜〜〜っ 何犬ですか〜〜〜!?
What kind of dog?
Wow!
すごーいっ
ほえー
A dog!
犬!
She's really different.
こいつって……

People often compare me to a fish.
よく魚類って言われるんですけどー
A scorpion fish, for example
〝おこぜ〟とかー

An unlikely siren.
相当…… いや かなりヤバイかも
ホニュー類ってはじめてー
Never been a mammal.

Shinichi
〝シンイチー〟
which bath toy do you think is nicer?
〝おフロのおもちゃ どれがいいと思う——?〟
ニヤハハ
Tee-hee-hee

She reminds me of Prof. Vieira.

ヴィエラ先生に似てる

Nodame

のだめ!

せんぱい…？
Chiaki?

こいつには絶対特別なものがある
she definitely has something special.

そして
And

こいつに合わせられるのは
I'm about the only one

オレ様ぐらいだ！
who can play with her.

ダーン
BONG

They're in perfect unison so far.
ここまでは
完璧なユニゾン
The real challenge lies in the next part
問題は次——
where the second piano has to play the main theme practically solo.
セカンド・ピアノが
ほとんど単独で
主題を……
うぅ
Oops!

もうキレ始めた
あの口
That mouth.
She's beginning to lose it.
Just when I tell her to play freely.
Docile creature...
自由にしろって言ったとたん 素直な奴……
でも
But...
合わせてみせる
I'll keep up.
でた!
Here we go.
ホラ飛んだ!
There, she missed it.
Hmm...
ぶ……っ
Skipped it!
はねた!
もうこいつのクセは知ってる
I know all her tricks now.

Amazing.
Long ago Prof. Vieira said that
once in a blue moon you perform so well you get goose bumps.
I'd been dreaming of such a moment
and all but given up until yesterday.
すご……!
昔 ヴィエラ先生が言ってた
身震いするほど感動する演奏ができることなんて本当にまれだって
オレは そんな瞬間を 夢見ながら
昨日までは あきらめてた

But right now
でも今たしかに
I feel little goose bumps.
小さな身震いを感じてる——
Bravo!
ブラボー
Clap, clap, clap
パチ
パチ
パチ
Bravo!
ブラボー!
I'm happy for you, Chiaki.
よかったねえ千秋くん
Looks like a penny has dropped.
なんか壁超えたみたいで
Clap, clap
パチ
パチ
Excuse me?
え?

オレのためのレッスンだったのか――
So the lesson was for me.
先輩の背中……
あのタヌキ教師……
Sly old fox.
あぢィ
Goodness!
ハア…
Sigh
My heart is going pitter-pat!
I want to hug you!
とびつきたくてドキドキ♡
えっ
What?
これってフォーリンラブ♡ですか!?
Could it be I'm falling in love?
発情～
Hormones surging
ちがう!
NO!
断じてちがう!
It certainly does not.
はう――胸がキューーンって苦しい…
Oh, I've got heartache!
こんな気持ちはじめてー…
Never felt like this before.
オレは日本(ここ)でもっとやれることがある
There is still work for me here in Japan.

Lesson 4

学校法人桃ヶ丘音楽学園
桃ヶ丘音楽大学大学院
桃ヶ丘音楽大学
Momogaoka College of Music
Graduate Studies
Undergraduate Studies
Ordinary.
平凡!
So ordinary.
平凡!

They're all so ordinary!
No, no, his family owns Uraken, the Chinese restaurant.
What!
You mean the one behind the school?
Yes, yes.
He's the son and heir.
Clomp, clomp
Is he on a delivery?
Um, don't think so. That's not a delivery bag.
Who's that guy?
Rice bowl and liver with leeks too.
Their egg fried rice is scrumptious.
Oh, I'm hungry.
Let's have lunch.
Nakata?

みーんな平凡！

あー　あの人
"裏軒(うらけん)"の
お兄ちゃんだよー！

裏軒って……
あの学校の裏の
中華屋さん!?

そーそー！

そこの息子さん

じゃあ
出前？

え〜〜　でもあのバッグ
おか持ちじゃないでしょう？

うわ〜〜なに？　あの人

中華丼に
レバニラも〜

あ——
おなかへって
きた〜〜

お昼に
しよう！

ナ、カ、タ？

あそこのチャーハン
めちゃくちゃおいしいん
だよね〜〜♡

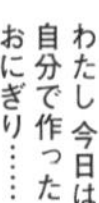

わたし今日は
自分で作った
おにぎり……

I made rice balls today.

ガタッ

Clatter

のだめ——!!

NODAME!

ドロボー!

Thief!

まてコラーッ

Wait, oy!

ヴァイオリン科2年　峰 龍太郎(みね りゅうたろう)(21)

おいっ　文化祭でやるバンドの曲なんにしよーか？
Hey, what's our band gonna play at the school fair?
Ha-ha-ha-ha!
オリジナルやる？
How about one of my originals?
オレ30曲作ってあんだ
I've composed 30.
それより峰……
Um, Ryutaro...
来週ヴァイオリンの試験だろ？
Don't you have a violin exam next week?
そんなエレキばっかやってて大丈夫かよ？
Should you really be faffing around on an electric violin?
また留年したら　どーすんだ
What if you have to stay back a year again?
せっかくオレが頼んでやった試験のためのピアノ伴奏者
That pianist I found for you—
おまえ逃げられたんだって？
I heard he quit.
N-No!
ちっ　ちがう！　あれは……
You've got it wrong!
ポーン
Plink
へたくそ
Crap.

不愉快だ！
帰る

It's offensive. I'm off.

顔を洗って出直してこいっ

Come back when you're in better shape.

あの
"千秋"って
やつが

That asshole Chiaki

オレの鋭い感性についてこれないから……

couldn't keep up with my cutting-edge style.

あいつめちゃピアノうまいって聞いたけど…

Oh? Apparently he's a brilliant pianist.

いいから別のやつ紹介してくれよ！

Just find me someone else, OK?

もっとテクがあって柔軟で

Someone with more technique but more flexible.

やさしくて

Kind too

オレの感性（センス）についてこれる芸術家肌の人間を!!

A true artist who knows how I think.

キュイーン

G-eee

な……
なんだ？

電源
切れてる

くそっ

だれだぁー！
Bang!
Who the hell
disconnected the
延長コード
extension cord?
切ったやつ……
ぎ……
G-
ぎゃぼ——!!
Gulp!
Munch
もがー
Oh! And I almost made it to the filling!
具まであと ひと口だったのにィ〜〜!!
しかも たらこだったのにィ
And it was cod roe!
おいっ
Hey!

きみ……ピアノ科?
You're a piano major?
CHOPIN
Nocturne, op.9-2
ハイ? そーですケド…
Yes, so?
いや
Nothing
かわいい!?
Cute!
あの……
Um...
今度オレの試験の伴奏……お願いできるかな?
Can I ask you to accompany me for my exam?
だれでもいいんじゃねーか! おまえはっ
In other words, you don't care who it is.
試験の伴奏?
Accompany you for your exam?
Megumi Noda, 20. Sophomore, majoring in piano.
ピアノ科2年
野田 恵(20)

SWEET HOUSE
ジャアアア
Hissss
ブツブツ…
Bubble
そろそろ
最終楽章……
Last movement coming up.
ピアノ科3年 千秋真一(21)
Shinichi Chiaki, 21.
Junior, majoring in piano.
ジュワーーッ
Sizzle
ビッ ビッ
Pop, hiss
できたな！
Done.
I know by the sound.
音でわかる
焼き加減！
ジュワー
ブシュー
Sizzle
Bubble
ピンポーン
Ding-dong!

ガチャッ
Click
突撃となりの晩ごはん〜〜〜♡
Excuse me, I'm from What's for Dinner Next Door?
by Yonesuke
ヒンよねすけー
はぁ…
Right
Oh, am I early?
あれ？ まだ早かったですか？
Nodame came over a lot these days.
最近 のだめがうちに頻繁に来るようになった——
Wow! Amazing!
ごあーっ すご〜〜い♡
What's this?
なんですかーこれっ
Chicken, Capri style.
地鶏のカプリ風！
ガンッ
Plonk
カプリ？
Capri?
Why the hell do I have to cook you dinner?
なんでオレがおまえにメシを与えなきゃいけないんだ!?
Night after night.
毎晩毎晩！

「美しい音楽は美しい生活から」でしょ♡
Doesn't exquisite music begin with exquisite food?
by 千秋
by Chiaki
いただきマースッ
Ooh, this looks good!
パン
Bread
自分で生活しろ——!!
Do your own cooking and cleaning.
またオレはボランティアをやっている
I'm doing charity work again.
はぅ はぅ
Gobble, gobble.
というのも 2週間前——
Two weeks earlier.
なんだ? これは……
What's this?
実家から送られてきたアジの干物にハート型マヨネーズ♡
My folks sent me some dried horse mackerel. I added the mayonnaise heart.
恋の出前大作戦♡です
True love delivered to your door!
のだめの手料理!
Nodame's home cooking.
アジです
Horse mackerel.
炭だろ!
It's completely burnt.
だからこの黒いのはなんだときいている!
I'm asking you what this black thing is.
まあひと口
Come on, try it.
殺す気か!?
Do you intend to poison me?

“手料理”というなら
If you're going to call it home cooking,
Boil, bubble
put a little effort into it.
これくらいのもの
Hiss
作ってから言え！
Like this.
Voila!
ぎゃああ!! なんですかーコレ!!
Wow! What's this?
ミレリーゲ・アラ・パンナコン・イ・ブロッコリ
Millerighe alla panna con e broccoli.
イタリア語
Italian
呪文料理!!
Mumbo, jumbo cuisine.
おいし〜〜〜!!
Yumm!
大きいマカロニだ〜
It's great big macaroni.
すごーい先輩!天才ー
You're amazing!
A genius!
お母さんよりうまいー!!
You're a better cook than my mother!
そ……そこまで
Oh, I wouldn't go that far.
アンブレーラ!! ※意味不明
Un preira.
*Gobbledygook
あ……あしたはもっとうまいの作ってやるよ
Um, tomorrow, I'll make you something even more tasty.
救世主ー
Savior!
キャー
Yippee!
のせられた
Sucker
はー
Oh,
ごちそーさまでしたー♡
thank you for a lovely meal.
こうして オレは不覚にものだめを餌付(えづ)けしてしまったのだった——
This is how I ended up feeding Nodame regularly.

Lounge
Mmm...
ふぁー
結婚って いいもんです ね~~~♡
WHO got married?
だれが 結婚した!?
Oh, Chiaki!
あ そーだっ先輩
Wedded bliss.
Do you know Beethoven's Violin Sonata No. 5 *Spring*?
ベートーヴェンのヴァイオリン・ソナタ5番〈春〉って知ってマス?
Yes. Why?
……知ってるけど なんで?
You accompany a violinist?
I'm going to accompany a violinist, so I've been practicing.
今度伴奏するんでさっき練習してたんですけどー
Sigh.
But I find it hard.
なんかよくわかんなくてー
Did you bring the score?
楽譜 持ってきた?
BEETHOVEN
Yes, I did.
ハイ! 持って きました
She blabbers on about love,
「恋」だとか なんとか言っておいて
Hmm.
OK, play it.
じゃあ弾いてみろよ
but she knows what matters.
こーゆーとこ しっかりしてるよな

メシが終わると
いつもピアノだ
After dinner, it's always piano.
That's completely wrong!
ギャヒー
Yikes!
全然ちがうじゃ
ねーか!!

Pant, pant
ハア
ハア
W-Wow!
す……すげ〜〜〜
We were in sync in one go.
一発であっちゃったよ……
She even got my mistakes.
まちがえたところまで…
Bravo, Nodame!
ブラボーのだめ!!
We're on exactly the same wavelength.
最高のフィーリングだ!!
Yesterday, Chiaki got so mad with me. Wow!
昨日は先輩にめちゃくちゃ怒られたのに
Really?
ほぇ〜〜〜?
Why?
なんで?
Your piano has soul.
きみのピアノにはソウルがある!
Soul?
ソール?
Yeah, soul.
魂(たましい)だ!

We have the same smell.
オレと同じ臭(にお)いがする!
We're ideal partners.
オレたちは最高のパートナーだ!
?
I knew it. The accompanying pianist was at fault.
やっぱり今まで伴奏者が悪かったんだ
OK, I play a quirky violin. But that doesn't mean I'm incompetent.
オレのヴァイオリンはクセはあってもヘタじゃない!
I know I'll pass this next exam.
今度の試験は絶対いける——!!
Anything the matter,
どうしたの?
Chiaki?
千秋くん

あ……

なんか今日は
気が乗らない
みたいだねー

野田くん
呼んでこようか？

Seems you're not into it today.
Shall I get Miss Noda?

ジョーダンやめてください!!

Lay off the jokes, please.
Guffaw
ハハハ
You sure?
そーかい？

少し……ちがう曲
弾いてもいいですか？

いいけど……？

ベートーヴェンのヴァイオリン・ソナタ——

あ……

アハハ
Laughter
バイバーイ
Bye!
またねー
See you!

千秋さまよ! 千秋さま!
It's Chiaki!
えーあの人が~
So that's him!
はー…
Sigh

今日のタメシ
なんにしよう……
What shall I make for dinner tonight?
キャー ため息〜
Ooh, he sighed!
なに悩んでるのかしら〜?
Penny for his thoughts.

魚—— この時期ならスズキ……
Fish. Hmm... Sea bass is in season.
かさご…… めばる
Scorpion fish, rock cod...

タイ…は高すぎだな なんにもめでたくないし……
Sea bream is too expensive.
Nothing to celebrate, anyway.

ぴぃきゃー
Eeek!

Hey!
え?

このアホな奇声は……
That idiotic shriek has to be...
Ha-ha-ha!
Chinese restaurant
中華
裏軒
Uraken
もが〜っ
Gobble

ぱかーん
POP
Here you go.
ハイよ!
Fried rice, Uraken style!
裏軒チャーハンおまち!
裏軒
裏軒
ドン
Plop
Wowmmm!
ぎゃほ——っ!!
(スゴーイ)
Fried dumplings too, Dad!
おやじィ 餃子(ギョーザ)もなー!!

スープ！
チャーハン
スープ！
な……
Soup!
Fried rice!
Soup!
What's going on?
のだめ！ どーだ？ うちの店の味は
How do you like our food, Nodame?
Gobble
そーか！ うまいか！
OK, so you like it.
のだめには
いつもタダで
食わせて
やるからなー
You can eat here free anytime.
いつでも
遊びに
来いよー!!
Drop by whenever you like.
なぁーおやじ!!
Right, Dad?
Ha-ha-ha
仕方ねーなぁ
Can't say no to
龍太郎の
〝運命の人〟
じゃあなー
your Miss Destiny.
おやじ
いいこと
言ったー！
Nice one, Dad!
運命ー
Destiny.
Hee-hee-hee
峰……
あれは……
ヴァイオリン科の
ヘタクソ……
That's Ryutaro,
that useless violinist.

So he's the one who asked Nodame to play piano.

あいつがのだめに伴奏頼んだのか——

まあ……強烈なヘタクソ同士

Fine. I wish those two monumental dunces

せいぜいがんばるがいいさ

all the best together.

新発売
たこ焼きのり弁当
人気商品
¥480

NEW Octopus Dough Balls and Seaweed Lunch box

やっぱり
来ねぇ……

No, she's not coming.

"どーだ？ うちの店の味は" はう〜〜♡

How do you like our food?

Gobble!

くっそ――
あの女ぁ〜〜

Damn that woman!

バキッ

Snap

エサがもらえれば どこだっていいんじゃねーか!!

She'll go anywhere to be fed.

ホーレ

Here, kitty.

ニャーン

Miaow

ニャヒー

Miaow

ケケケ

Mee-hee-hee!

I'm well rid of her.
バカバカしい！
A quiet night in for a change.
久しぶりの静かな夜だ
DIGITAL MASTERED
POYJ 1088
STEREO
COMPACT disc DIGITAL AUDIO
LUDWIG VAN BEETHOVEN
Sinfonie Nr.1 op.21 C-dur
conducting by
SEBASTIANO VIEIRA
Tonight I will listen to Prof. Vieira's new Beethoven recording.
今日はヴィエラ先生の新作でベートーヴェン・ナイトだ！

4:58 TRACK 1
ピンポーン
Ding-dong
ピンポンピンポンピンポーン
Ding-dong Ding-dong Ding-dong
Dammit!
How much more does she want to annoy me?
くそっ!!
どこまで
人をおちょくれば……

コラーッ
めくそ!! (のだめ)
NO-DAMMIT, you eyesore!
BANG
こんな
遅くに……
What time do you think it is...?
なんの
What
用……
do you want...?

彩子……!?
Saiko!
めくそって……
Eyesore?
ヒドイ……
How cruel!
声楽科3年 多賀谷彩子(21)
Saiko Tagaya, 21. Junior, majoring in voice.
ち……ちがう!!
N-No!
それは おまえのこと じゃなくて……
I didn't mean you.
グス…
Sniff
So Eyesore
is your new girl-friend?
じゃあ…… 新しい彼女?
そんなわけねーだろ…
OF COURSE NOT!
めくそさん

とにかく……
中に入れよ
Look, come in.
彩子
Saiko.

裏軒
↑おかもち
(千秋のお土産)
Uraken take-out for Chiaki

バターン…
Slam
ガーン……
Oh my God!

Lesson 5

★Basic training in rhythm, melody and harmony.

※ソルフェージュ＝リズム，メロディ，ハーモニーの基礎訓練。

I'm gutted.
どガーーン……
She stayed the night.
昨日泊まったんですね……
So you had a girlfriend.
彼女いたんですか……
Nodame!
のだめーー!
You know that Fall in Love lipgloss from Mabelle that you said you wanted?
あんたが欲しいって言ってたマ・ベールの「恋するグロス」
I got it for you.
買ってきてやったわよーー♡

のだめ……？
Nodame?
このチュルチュルグロスでだれかにキスしてもらうんじゃなかったっけ？
Didn't you say this "moist and silky gloss" would be sure to get you kissed?
涙→
Tears
ゲ…昨日と同じ服…
Uurgh, she was wearing the same dress yesterday.
絆（きずな）……
Soul... mates.
はぁ〜〜〜？
Excuse me?
おーーっ のだめ〜〜
Hey, Nodame!
練習しよーぜ！
Let's practice!
練習！
Practice!

※きわめて速く。火のように。 ★Fast as fire.

の……
のだめ!?
N-Nodame!
おいっ
Hey!
Sigh
どうした!?
おまえのソウルは……
What's happened to your soul?
Your spirit?
魂(たましい)は!?
クス…
Sad chuckle
それは幻(まぼろし)……
Just a dream.
恋……
Love...
千秋先輩……
Chiaki...

むらさきの
バラの人……

し……

失恋か!!

くそー！

なんでこんな時に！

どこのどいつだ!?

先輩……

このガッコの

オレがくっつけてやる!!

試験は来週なんだ！

失恋なんぞで
へこまれたら
演奏にさしさわる！

Oh,
あ
there he is.
いた！
Who?
どれ？
The one reading on the bench.
あの……ベンチで本読んでる人
What?
え……
That's
あれは……
Chiaki.
千秋……
You know him?
え〜〜〜 峰くん知ってるの!?
Shinichi!
Why waste yourself on that—
なんでおまえ あんな……
GREEN

待った〜〜〜？
Have I kept you waiting?
べつに… No.
なに読んでたの？
What are you reading?
あれが のだめのライバルか？
That is your rival?
コクコク
Nod, nod
負けだ……
Well, you've lost.
あれは多賀谷彩子
That's Saiko Tagaya.
えっ
What?
美人で優秀な声楽科のマドンナ！
The beautiful, brilliant star of the Voice Department.
しかも「多賀谷楽器」のお嬢さまだ!!
And her family owns Tagaya Instruments.
あんないい女とつきあっている千秋がおまえに振り向く可能性は万にひとつもないだろう！
If she's Chiaki's girlfriend, you haven't got a chance.

というわけで
潔くあきらめて

練習
しよう！

追い討ち——!!

ねえ真一

今日もどっか
飲みにいき
ましょーよ♡

オレ今日……

部屋で自分の練習したいんだけど

I
want to stay in and practice today.
Uur
二日酔い
Hangover

なによー！
いいでしょっ

わたしだって
真一が腐ってるとき
さんざんつきあって
やったじゃない！

今日は 帰らない わよ――！
I'm not going home today.
やめろ～
Cut that out.
彩子は―― オペ研が今度やる オペラ公演〈魔笛〉の "夜の女王" 役を
In this year's Opera Club production, *The Magic Flute*, the title role went to an obese girl.
Queen of the Night
〈夜の女王〉→ ソプラノの主役
One of the most coveted soprano roles.
それまでライバルとも 思っていなかった 巨漢の女に奪われたらしい
Someone Saiko hadn't even thought of as a rival.
血のにじむような努力でトップの座を死守してきた彩子は
Saiko had fought tooth and nail to attain her spot as diva.
なにかが プチンと 切れたようだ
It seemed this setback had plunged Saiko into despair.
Bang
なんであのブー子（こ）が"夜の女王"なのよ!!
How can a hippo play the Queen of the Night?
うぃー
Weep

There are those who leapfrog ahead after the penny drops.
ある日突然なにかを摑(つか)んで急成長するやつっているからな
And how come I play her daughter?
しかもなんでわたしがあいつの娘役なわけぇ～
I want to go home and practice.
オレも帰って練習がしたい……
I haven't touched the baton recently,
最近指揮棒振ってない
Look,
おいっ
you've had enough.
いい加減にしとけよ！
You know that smoking and drinking are bad for your voice.
酒とタバコはのどに悪いんだろ
Mmm...
フフフ
So is sex.
セックスもね～♡
If that's what's on your mind,
そういう話なら……
talk to your boyfriend.
彼氏にしろよ！
listened to CDs,or watched the videotape of the Vienna Philharmonic...
聴(き)きたいCD録画しておいたウィーン・フィル……

はあ？ 彼氏ィ〜〜〜？
What? Boyfriend?
いるだろ！ 指揮科の…… ハムみたいなやつ
You know, the conducting major who looks like a leg of ham.
早川くん!?
Hayakawa?
やだ〜〜っ 彼氏じゃないわよ！ 早川くん……
Yuck! He's not my boyfriend!
彼のお母さんが声楽家だからちょっと仲良くなっただけで……
We just had something in common, as his mother sings.
なによ それ！
How could you?
え……ちがうの？
So you're not together?
あ〜〜
I get it.
そっか だから真一
That's why you
最近連絡してこなかったんだー
haven't called me lately.
クスクス
Chuckle
ちがうって……
No, it's not that.
忘れてた だけだ
Actually, I'd forgotten about her.
ねぇ……わたしたち
Shinichi, why don't we
ヨリ 戻さない？
get back together again?

ガタッ
Clatter
負けメス犬はキライだ
I don't like losers.
な……
What?
仕返しってわけじゃないけど——
I'm not getting back at you.
なによオー!
How dare you!
自分がなにかに夢中になってるとき足引っぱられるのって
When you're focused on something,
うっとーしーもんなんだな
it's distracting to be around people who pull you down.
オレもちょっとまえまではああだったのか
I must have been like that until recently.
さむ…
Brrr
反省…
Ashamed

SWEET HOUS
202
千秋
202 CHIAKI
酒くさ
Pfoar alcohol!
ガララ
Rattle
のだめのピアノ……
Nodame's playing.
それから
And
あいつか!!
he's with her.

いい加減立ち直れ！
全然だめ――!!
That's hopeless.
Nodame!
のだめ――!!
Get a grip!
Music is all you've got left.
Shock
おまえにはもうピアノしか、ないんだろ!?
So at least play the piano well.
Your raison d'etre is—
Show some life.
Pew! Your hair stinks.
生きてる証(あかし)を示せ
せめてピアノぐらいまともに弾かなきゃ
おまえの存在価値は……
おいくせーぞあたま！

いや……ごめん
Sorry.
つい……
It just came out.
本音が…
The truth
……なぁ
Look,
それならいっそ
why don't you just
オレとつきあわねーか?
go out with me instead?
だよなー
Guess not.
Ha-ha-ha
じゃあとりあえずヤケ食いでもするか?
OK. When in doubt, pig out.
今日もたくさん持ってきてやったぞ!
As usual, I brought loads.
裏軒
Uraken
ほれっ チャーハンに餃子(ギョーザ)!
Fried rice, fried dumplings.
麻婆(マーボー)ナスに麻婆豆腐に麻婆春雨!
Eggplant in chilli sauce. Tofu in chilli sauce. Vermicelli in chilli sauce.
のだめの好きな麻婆づくしだぞ〰♡
An absolute feast of your favorite things.
先輩に会いたい……
I want to see him.
うぐ…
Weep

千秋先輩の料理が食べたい〰〰!!
I want Chiaki's home cooking.
びー
Sob
千秋の料理〰〰!?
Chiaki's home cooking?
なんだそりゃ
What do you mean?
カプリなんとかにブロッコリなんとか……
Capri something, broccoli something.
愛の呪文(じゅもん)料理……
Mumbo jumbo loveboat cuisine.
おまえ……
You mean
千秋に料理してもらってたのか!?
Chiaki cooks for you?
ごはんだよー
Din-dins!
す……すげぇ!!
Wow!
あの男に料理……
You got him to cook?
のだめ!
Nodame!
それって脈あるんじゃねーのか!?
I think you might have a chance.
ミャク……?
Chance?
普通キライな女に料理なんかしねーって
Men only cook for women they fancy.
そうかな……?
You think so?
そーだよ!
Yeah.
もしかしてがんばれば彼女から千秋を奪えるかもしれねーぞ!
Make an effort and he might switch over to you.
OVEN

How?
Switch over? An effort?
どうやって!?
奪う！
Sleep with him.
オレなら……寝盗(ねと)る！
Sleep with him?
寝盗る!!
そう！　女の武器を使って直接 男の本能に訴えかける
Use your female charms to appeal to his masculinity.
"Take moi, I am fresh fruit."
″わたしは新鮮な果実よ♡″
Men (i.e., me) inevitably fall for it.
男は(オレは)そーゆーのに最も弱い！
Female charms?
女の武器
Fresh fruit?
果実！
Is what monsieur suggests.
だっちゅーの♡
うふん
Ooh-la-la!
さきイカ
Shredded Squid

もっと
色っぽい服は
ねーのか!?
Haven't you got a sexier dress?
え
What?
古い!
Out of date
しかも
キモイ!!
and creepy!
夏服ならー……
Um, I have a summer dress.
まぁ……
服はそれで
いいとして
The dress will do.
顔が……
Next, your face.
顔!?
Face?
のだめ 化粧品とか持ってねーの?
Do you own any makeup?
持ってマス!!
Yes!
友達から
借りたの
いっぱい!
My friends lent me all this stuff.
↑盗ったともいう
Also known as stealing.
カチャ
カチャ
Rattle, rummage
う〜〜ん……
Yeah...

こんな感じでしたよね？
Do I look like
Marilyn Monroe?
マリリン・モンローって
Outdated!
古い！
も……
もう少しソフトにしたほうがいいんじゃねーか？
A-
Aim for a more subtle look.
全体的にボカシ入れて
Blur the edges.
ゴシ ゴシ
Scrub Scrub
泣くなー！
Don't cry!
泣きたいのはこっちだ——
I'm the one who feels like crying.
I'm smiling.
笑ってマス!!
Shit!
くそー！
OK. Reapply the foundation.
もう一度上からファンデを乗せて……

Bet Chiaki's a sex maniac under that cool exterior.
千秋はムッツリスケベそうだから
Try a natural look.
もう少し自然な感じにしてー……
Cool exterior? Sex maniac? Natural?
ムッツリは自然？
Yeah.
ああ！
He'll fall for nature and hormones rather than something too contrived.
あからさまなアピールよりナチュラルなフェロモンが好みだろう……
Delicate eyebrows,
マユは少し弱々しく
large, bright eyes
目元はパッチリ
and a fresh, youthful pink for the cheeks and lips.
頬(ほお)とくちびるはピンク色でさわやかに……
OK.
よし！
Done.
できた
Yippee!
やったー!!
I'm ready to seduce Chiaki.
これで千秋先輩を寝盗れますね♡
Hey!
おい……

What are you talking about,
なんの相談をしてるんだ?
you guys?
おまえら
ひィ
Yikes!
ポターン…
Plop
He's come
きてくれた
to see me.
わたしに会いに……
Chi...
ち……

CHIAKI!
Jesus!
I missed you so!
千秋せんぱぁい〜〜〜〜!!
会いたかったぁ
なっ……
W-
Hug
What on earth have you done to your face?
なんだ その顔は――!?
D-Do you feel like doing it?
む……ムラムラしますか?
↖かさねぬりしすぎ… ダッチワイフ風メイク
Too much makeup makes her look like a blow-up sex doll.

ドカー
Thump
ぎゃふん
Ow-eek
それより なんだ!?
I'd rather know
さっきの 演奏は!?
why you just played so badly?
聞くに 耐えん!
It was unbearable.
騒音! 近所迷惑だ!!
Noise pollution. Awful for the neighbors.
やる気あんのか!?
You serious?
ん?
はうー
Awwaagh
おまえのせいで
It's your fault.
おまえの せいだろー のだめが……!
Your fault that Nodame's like this.
使いものに ならなく…
She's useless.
ちょっと まて——!!
Hang on.

You...
おまえ……
You really think you're good?
本気で自分がうまいと思ってンの？
Of course!
と……当然だ！
I placed third in the nationwide juniors competition.
オレは全国のジュニアコンクールで3位になったことだってあるんだぞ！
いつの話だ…
When?
They labelled you a prodigy and you got the wrong idea?
それで「神童」とか言われて勘違いしたのか
Often happens.
よくある話だ
Hand over that violin.
ちょっとそのヴァイオリン貸してみろ
What!
え……

〈春〉……
Spring
ブン
Twang, twang
ブン
さわりぐらいでいいだろ……
Just a taste, OK?

バカうま———!!
Phenomenal!
すごーい!! 先輩ーっ
Wow, Chiaki!
The violin too!
Ohaargh!
ヴァイオリーーン!!
I won a junior competition too. In Vienna.
ジュニアなら……オレもウィーンのコンクールで優勝したことあるんだよな
Love you
Love you
Vienna?
You won?
ウィーン…… 優勝!!
I can give you a few tips, if you like.
少しなら教えてやってもいいけど?

Lesson 6

Pop, jazz, rock...
Many violinists quit classical for these other pastures.
ポップス　ジャズ　ロック……　クラシック界から飛び出し活躍するヴァイオリニストはたくさんいる——
And...
で
you plan to be one of them. Am I right?

おまえも
そのひとりに
なろうってのー
——？

悪いか
——!?
Anything wrong with that?
別に……
No.
やりたきゃ
ロックでも
なんでもやればいい
Do whatever you like be it rock...
学校です
Nodame's forgotten they're at school
やってるよ！
I'm doing it!
作曲とか色々…
Composing etc.
だからオレは
もうクラシックなんて
どーでもいいんだ！
So I don't give a damn about classical music!
試験だって
再試くらわなきゃ
それでいいんだよ
I don't give a damn about exams as long as I don't fail.
おまえに教わることはなにもない！
You've nothing to teach me.
行くぞ！ のだめ
Nodame, we're off!
あー
Aargh!
ブチブチブチッ
Snap, pop, snap
わーっ
Ooh!
キャー
Yikes!
千秋さまー
Chiaki!
どうせ
言われることは
わかってる！
Anyway, I know what he's going to say.

やれ リズムだ 音程だ
Rhythm, pitch,
曲を楽譜どおりに正確に！
play exactly according to the score.
いつもそうだ
Always the same:
Technique, technique, play accurately...
テクニック テクニック！ 正確に！
いくら自分なりに曲を表現しようと努力しようと 1ヵ所の間違いを追及される
You can bend over backwards expressing the piece, but they'll penalize you for one mistake.
だからクラシックはキライだ！
That's why I hate the world of classical music.

のだめ
ますますこの曲が
わかりませ——ん!!
I'm even
more
lost!
ベートーベン〜〜っ
〈春〉ってなんジャー
What on earth
is Beethoven's
Spring!
BEETHOVEN
SONATA NO.5 IN F MAJOR, OP. 24
202
千秋
202
CHIAKI
その
茶わんは
なんだ…
What's that
bowl for?
おまえな〜〜
If you're
lost,
BEETHOVEN
Violin Sonatas
at least try
to listen to
a CD.
わからないなら
CDぐらい
聴(き)けよ!
BEETHOVEN

わたしと
峰くんのと
My version and Ryutaro's
全然
ちがいマス……
are entirely different.
これが〈春〉——
So this is *Spring.*
おまえたちのは〈正月〉——
More like New Year Bash when you guys play it.
ちく
ちく
Stitch, stitch
縫い物の最中(ボタン付け) Sewing on buttons
Chiaki...
Could you play the violin,
クゥーン
Please? Wuff, wuff!
……先輩 ちょっとヴァイオリン弾いてみてくれませんか?
1回だけだぞ
Just once.
また
ボランティアだ……
Here I am volunteering again.
最初の八分音符少し長めに
OK. Extend the first one-eighth note a bit.
いくぞ
Here goes.

She's only heard the CD once.
1回CD聴いただけでこれだ……
She's awesome.
恐ろしい奴（やつ）……

Wow!
くっ……
Oh...
あへ〜〜〜……
That felt so good.
気持ちよかったデス……♡
Drop the weird voice.
妙(みょう)な声を出すな!!
はうん〜…
Oh, honey
I had my hands full just trying to keep us together.
I haven't played the violin recently.
最近弾いてなかったし
No good. Out of practice.
やっぱダメだな
オレはあわせるのでいっぱいいっぱい……
But you're brilliant, Chiaki!
え〜〜〜っ!? すごくうまいですヨー千秋先輩!
Well,
maybe it's better than my piano.
あ—— まあ……まだピアノよりは上かもな……
You're joking!
ぷあー!?
?
?
Don't dwell on it.
深く考えんでいい
You wouldn't understand anyway.
どうせわかるまい

It didn't work at all with Ryutaro.
峰くんとはうまくあわせられなかったのに……
I wonder why.
なんでだろー？
Still, he did say it felt good.
でも峰くんは〝気持ちよかった〟って——
Right.
……ああ
It's called
そーゆーのはいわゆる……

Musical masturbation.
オナニープレイってゆーんだよ！
You know,
デスよ
playing for your own gratification.
意味はひとりよがり
Excuse
は……
me?
はい？

それから──
峰くんは
アンサンブルが
なってねぇ！
You also don't know how to play
in an ensemble.
デス！
ピアノの音
ちっとも聴いてないだろ!?
You're not listening to the piano at all.
ひとりで
気持ちよく
走って
どうする!?
What's the point of cheerfully going off on your own?
デスヨ
それから〜〜〜
And
don't try to be a technical virtuoso.
テクニックにばっか気をとられるな！
ふい〜〜〜…
以上4つ！
のだめからの、アドバイスでした──♡
These are my four
bits of advice.
じゃあ 今言ったことをキモに銘じて
Keep that advice in mind
and once more from the top.
もう一回
最初から
やりましょ──
Off the chest
スッキリ－
カラ──ン…
Clank
え……？
What's up?

Don't try to be a technical virtuoso.
"テクニックにばっか気をとられるな！"
Acting as if he knows it all.
なにもかも見透かしたように……
That's why I hate the world of classical music.
だからイヤなんだこの世界……
You can bust your gut only to have a joker like Chiaki tear you to shreds.
いくらがんばっても　千秋のようなふざけた奴がポロッと出てきて　やる気を失わさせる
Chiaki? A joker?
ふざけた…？千秋先輩が？
Yes. Look at him!
だってそーだろ！　ピアノ科でピアノもあんなにうまいくせに
He's a brilliant piano major.
But he is also a crack violinist—that's dodgy.
ヴァイオリンもうまいなんてインチキだー！
Well, Chiaki is a genius.
だって――　千秋先輩は天才でショ♡
It's not that simple!
一言で片づけんな――!!
How dare you patronize me!
ば……馬鹿にしやがって……！
OK, I'm a dunce.
どうせオレはヘタクソだよ！
I've got no talent.
才能なんかね――よ！

峰くんて……

Ryutaro...

Weep, weep

ガラスのように繊細なんですネ

I didn't realize you were so sensitive.

ほっとけ!!

Leave me alone!

でも……千秋先輩 峰くんのことヘタなんて言ってませんでしたよ～?

Still, Chiaki didn't say you were a dunce.

「表現がおもしろい」とか

In fact he said you were "expressive"

「アンサンブルはダメだけどソロはいい」とか

and "no good at ensembles but

ホメてたし——

good at solos."

千秋……

Chiaki...

ね♡ だから練習しよー 峰くん

So come on, Ryutaro. Let's practice.

ちゃんとあえばとっても気持ちいい曲ですよ——〈春〉!

Spring will be such a pleasant piece once we manage to play together.

お花畑です——♡

Flowery meadows.

Nodame...
のだめ……
やめてくれよ「花畑」なんて幼稚なイメージで弾くの……
Don't play to such a girly image.
Beethoven would turn in his grave.
ベートーベンに失礼だぜ…
What?
ええ～
What then?
じゃあどんなイメージ？
Maybe lightning
おれは「光る青春の喜びと稲妻（いなずま）」——
and the shining joyful blaze of youth.
かな♡
Yuck! Why lightning?
げえ～
なんでイナズマ～～!?
Shut up. Just play like that, OK?
うっせー！そう弾けばいいんだよ！
The violin nut and the piano nut...
ヴァイオリン・バカに
ピアノ・バカ……

How will they do in the exam?

さて試験はどーなるやら

試験当日——

おいっ
Hey!
もう学校行くんじゃ……
Isn't it time for school?
のだめ……？
N-Nodame?
なにやってンだ!?
Why are you lying there?
ひっ
Yikes!
ハアハア…
Pant, pant
あぅ〜〜〜
Uurgh, I'm sick.
カゼ!?
COLD?
おまえ……そういえば なんでそんな薄着ばっか……
Come to think of it, why have you been dressing for summer?
秋だぞ！今
It's fall now.
ジュー
Sizzle
げ……
Uurgf
おまえ……なに食った!?
Did you eat anything bad?
カゼです〜〜〜
I've got a cold.

お……お色気で勝負しようと思って……♡
I thought I'd seduce you by showing a bit of skin...
ゲハっ
Whatcha-doin'?
What the hell?
ええ――っ
Nodame has a cold?
のだめがカゼ――!?

ん
とりあえず持ってきたから……
I've brought her anyway.
Yep.
んって……
Yep?
こんな死んだイモ虫みたいなのどーしろって言うんだよ——!!
She's like a dead caterpillar? How can I perform with that?
知るか——!!
Don't ask me!
ど……どーした? のだめ!
N-Nodame, what's going on?
ハァ ハァ
Pant, pant
……
……
ハァ ハァ
Pant, pant
……
……
そうか…… わかった!
OK.
I get it.
王子様がキスしてくれれば治るかもしれないそーだ
She says she might get better if her prince kisses her.
もういい……わかった
All right, all right.

峰のピアノはオレが弾く！
I'll accompany you on the piano.
一発勝負だ！
It's all or nothing!
そんなー
Impossible!
やっぱりィー
I knew it!
Exam room, Violin Dept.
ヴァイオリン科
試験会場
へぇ——…
うまいな
コイツ
Hey! He's really good.

あれはヴァイオリン科でいちばんうまい中村(なかむら)——
That's our top violinist, Nakamura.
あ——……毎日 朝から晩まで学校で練習してる奴か!
I know. The one who practices at school from dawn 'til dusk.
なんで順番あいつの後なんだよ!
Why did I end up right after him?
来月からウィーンに留学するんだってよ
Apparently next month he's leaving for Vienna.
ブル ブル
Tremble, shake
なにィっ
What?
くそっ ウィーンだと〰!?
Vienna?
Damn him.
負かしてやる!
We'll beat him.
負かせるわけねーだろ!!
How? It's impossible.
フン
Huh!
少なくとも相方のピアノよりオレのほうがうまいぞ
At least I'm a better pianist than his guy.

……いいよな
努力しないでも報われてる奴は……
It must be nice.
Must be nice for those who do well without even trying.
はあ〜〜〜？
Excuse me?
言うこと大きくて
Those who can afford to be patronizing.
言っておくけどオレ……
I'll have you know
ヴァイオリンもピアノも3歳の時から ず〜〜っとやってたんだぞ
that I've been playing both violin and piano since I was 3.
特にヴァイオリンは大学に入るまで それこそ朝から晩まで
Especially the violin. I practiced from dawn to dusk until I started college.
えっ……
What?
血ヘド出るくらい厳しい先生だったしな
With a tutor so strict it was all blood,
sweat and tears.
それに比べてピアノは苦手で——
In comparison, I wasn't that good at piano.
だから大学はピアノ科に入ったんだ
So I enrolled here as a piano major.
まぁ かなり真剣にやったから 2年でトップになれたけど
I did apply myself, so in two years I got top ranking.
今は少しさぼり気味かな……
But I've slacked off a bit for the moment.

今は作曲の勉強がいちばんで

本当にヤな奴……

オイ……なにが言いたいんだ……結局

結局……

オレは指揮者になるのが夢なんだ

だからいろいろ勉強してるけど……

まだ　なにひとつ報われてねーよ!

指揮……
Conducting?
Hey!
次——!
Next!
峰くん!
Ryutaro Mine!
早く来なさい
Quick!
いくぞ
Wish us luck!
え!?
What?
今日はテクニックとか そんなに気にするな!
Don't worry about technique etc. today.
でも
オレ様の音は
ちゃんと
聴いとけよ——
Just listen when I'm playing
あとは
てきとーに
and have fun.
好きに弾いて
いいから
Play however you like.
ガラッ
Rattle

ヴァイオリン・ソナタ第5番ヘ長調作品24〈春〉―― ベートーヴェンが耳疾(じしつ)に悩まされながらも 女をとっかえ引っかえ遊んでいたころに作られたと思われる 幸せそーな曲

Flash
It's supposed to be *Spring*!
〈春〉なのに……

ホ〜

Interesting

Cheeky bastard...

I tell him to have fun and he does.

ったく…… 好きにしろって言ったとたん 素直な奴！

He's all over the place—like Nodame.
のだめといっしょでメチャクチャだ
Still, I'll rise to the challenge.
でも……あわせてみせる!
Wow!
すごい
He comes in just when I want him to.
来てほしいときに来る……
Chiaki conducts.
千秋が指揮する
I feel really safe.
すごい安心……
I feel good.
気持ちがいい——

Flowery meadows...
花畑——
Amazing.
Shinichi Chiaki is indeed tremen-dous.
Ha-ha-ha
I found it so moving.
やっぱり 千秋くんて すごいです ねー
いや—— しかし
まったく…… 感動しましたよ
Few can accompany such a violin.
Oh, yes, yes, Ryutaro Mine!
How shall we grade him?
あんな演奏に あわせられる なんてねぇ
ああ……峰くん
どうしますか？ 彼の評価……
I found them a very good-looking duo.
Yes, I thought so too!
でも……あのふたり すごくルックスのよいユニットでしたね——
ああ！ それ わたしも思いました！
教官室
Tutors' office
Real power!
Yes, I felt my heart pounding.
Guffaw
カッコイ～
Really cool!
ドキドキ しちゃい ましたよ——
迫力あった ね——

峰——！
Oy, Ryutaro!
オレ　ゲーム会社の内定出たんだよ〜〜!!
I've got a job with the computer game company!
やったー
Yippee!
いや〜もう！
I'm glad
さっさとピアノに見切りをつけて
I cut my losses with the piano
打ち込み系ばっかやっててよかった〜〜
and concentrated on computer games.
もうこれでしばらく遊べるぜ！
I can goof off now.
おまえも試験ＯＫだったんだろ!?
You did OK on the exam, right?
バンドやろーよ
Let's have a gig.
文化祭でやるっつー曲決まった？
Got that piece you wanted for the fair?
悪いけど
Sorry.
バンドは解散する
I want to disband.
え？
What?
オレはクラシック一本で生きてゆく——
I've decided to focus on classical music.

千秋真一(21)
報われない
ボランティア
活動継続中──

タマゴスープ
持ってきたぞ──

だって──
のだめの部屋
健康によく
ないし──

Lesson 7

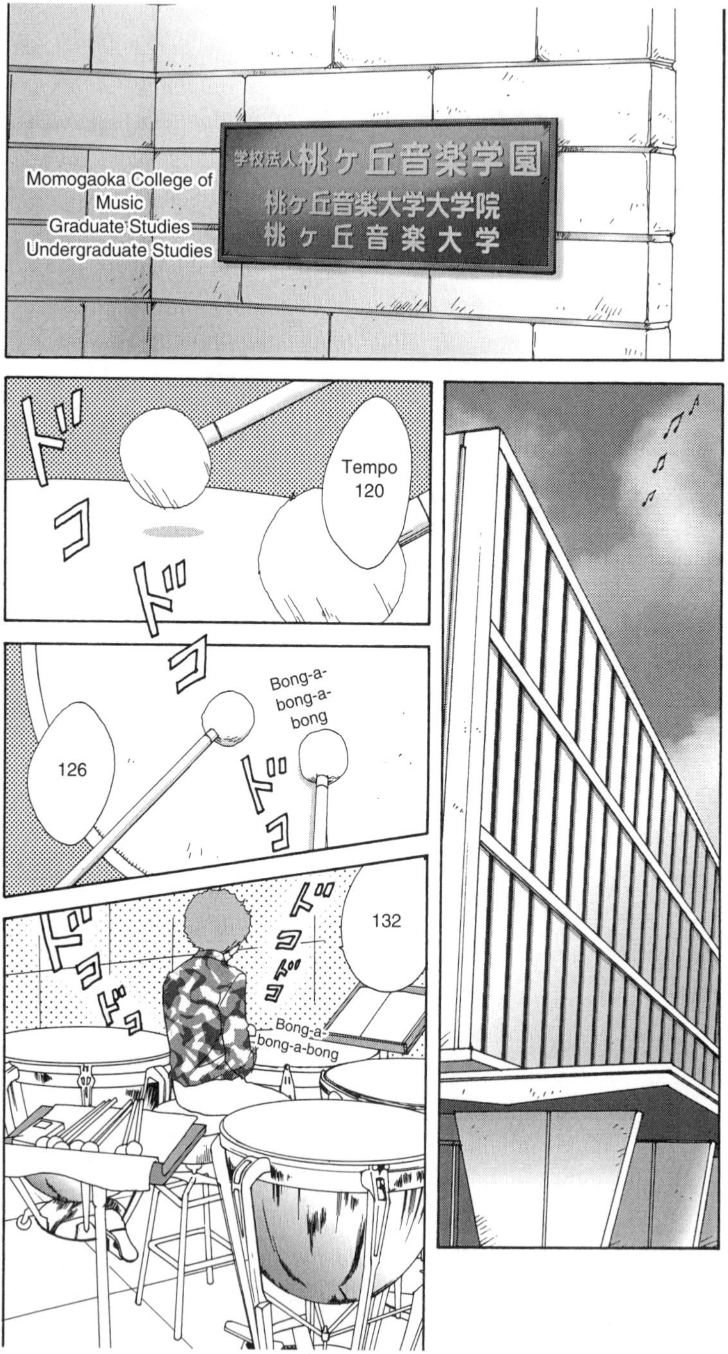

テンポ120

Tempo 120

Bong-a-bong-a-bong

126……

126

132……

132

Bong-a-bong-a-bong

162
ハァ
ハァ
ハァ
Pant; heave, pant
ドコドコドコドコッ
Bong-a-bong
バン
BANG!
Aaaargh!
いやぁぁあ———!!
I can't
bear it anymore!
もうっ 耐えられない!!
わ——っ
Sob

ど……どうしたんですか？ あの人
What's wrong?
ああ 真澄(ますみ)ちゃん
Masumi?
Guffaw
彼女は閉所恐怖症で 練習室が苦手なんだよ
He suffers from claustrophobia and hates the practice studios.
よくああなるんだ
Often gets like that.
でも彼女は ティンパニー すごいうまいんだぜ――
But Masumi's a crack timpanist.
Aオケだし
Plays for Orchestra A
マリンバや ドラムも……
Also fantastic on the marimba and drums.
自称"打楽器の女王"!
He's the self-styled "Queen of Percussion."
彼女、……
Queen
女王、……？
of Percussion?
もうイヤ！
No more!
山形へ帰りたい!!
I want to go home to Yamagata.

山形の
広い空の下で
暮らしたい！

I want to live under the open skies of Yamagata.

アハハ

Whee-hee-hee!

でも……

But

キャー

Squeal

千秋さまよっ

It's Chiaki!

あっ 本当だー

So it is!

ああ……

Oh...

千秋(ちあき)さま!?

Chiaki...

でもやっぱり 千秋さまのいる東京を…… この学校を離れられない わたし♡

But I can't leave this school or Tokyo when Chiaki is here.

すてき…

So gorgeous!

先輩これから
練習ですかー？

のだめ先輩のピアノ
聴(き)きたいです〜！

ピアノ科2年
野田恵(のだめぐみ)——

An orchestra...
オーケストラか……
What's up, Chiaki?
Penny for your thoughts?
どうしたんですか？ 元気ないですね なにか悩みが……？
Oh!
If it's about dinner tonight, I'd like a *nabe* stew.
あ!! 今日の夕ごはんなら お鍋(なべ)がいいデス♡
Whack!
Ow!
So he wasn't worried about dinner.
Swell
ごはんの献立に 悩んでるんじゃ なかったんだ……
Still...
でも……
He asked me to do the shopping.
Eeek! Yippee!
ごはんの買い物 頼まれちゃった〰♡
Such a close couple!
仲よし夫婦!!

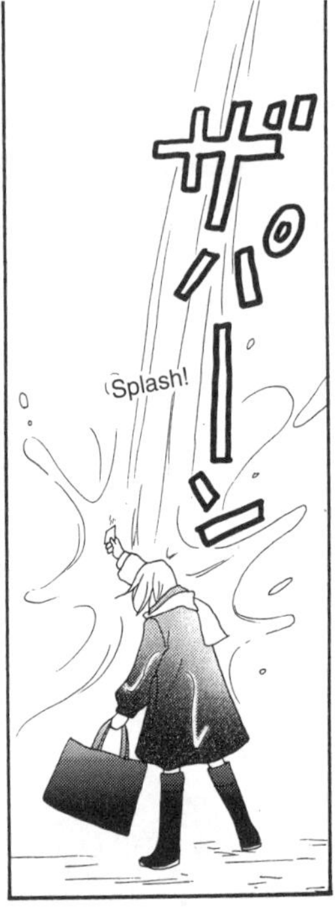

なんだ？ どーした!? 上から水とバケツが だれだよオイっ

あれ〜〜〜？

だれもいねーぞー

この手紙を2日以内に
100人に出さないと
おまえは死ぬ。
Unless you send this letter to 100 people within 2 days, you will die.
死んじゃえ
委員会より
The You're Dead Committee
手紙だ!
A letter!
洋子(ようこ)(母)かな!?
Maybe it's from Yoko (her mother).
202
千秋
202 CHIAKI
手紙書くの手伝ってくださ――い!!
Please help me write these letters!
わーん
Waargh!
レターセット
Envelopes and writing paper
アホか――!!
You idiot!
今どき不幸の手紙…
What sad creature sends spooky chain letters now?
ビデ
こんなの　ただのイタズラに決まってンだろ!!
This is just a practical joke.

いたずら……
だれが!?
Practical joke? Who?
知るか！
DUNNO!
死んじゃえ委員会
The You're Dead Committee
おまえ なにか
心当たりは
ないのか？
Can you think of anyone?
人にうらみをかうような……
Anyone hold a grudge against you?
ドロボー
Thief!
ドロボー
Thief!
↑昼メシ略奪すること28回
Guilty of 28 counts of lunch robbery.
マキちゃん
……？
Maki?
それとも
学食の
おばさん？
Or the woman in the cafeteria?
近所の
魚屋さん!?
Or the local fishmonger?
なにをやったんだ おまえは……
What on earth did you do?
それより 今日頼んだ
晩メシの食材は
どうした!?
By the way, did you do the shopping for dinner?
ちゃんと買ってきたのか？
You really got it all?
ああ……
ハイ！
ちゃんと買って
きました♡
Yes, I got it all.
でも……
買い物のメモが
水でにじんで
わからなくなって
I had trouble reading my shopping list, though. It got wet and blurry.
イナゴ
Locusts
ザーサイ
Chinese pickled vegetables
春巻
Spring rolls
解読できたのがこれだけで……
These are the only ones I could figure out.

オレは鍋の材料を
頼んだんだ——!!

マキちゃん ごめんなサーイ!!

わたしじゃないわよ!!

ずいぶん古典的なイヤガラセね〰〰

至近距離なのがスゴイ——

だれだか知らないけどいい気味だわ

これにこりたらもう 人の弁当盗(と)るんじゃないわよ!

それは約束できまセン!

でも今日は

ちゃんと自分のお弁当持ってきたんですヨ〜♡

昨日の夕食の残りものをつめこんだ

千秋先輩の愛妻弁当〰〰♡

はぁ〜〜〜?
Excuse me?
Chiaki?
千秋先輩…?
妄想 妄想
Delusion, delusion.
いつもの電波よ
You know, the usual unilateral telepathy.
いっただきま〜〜〜す♡
Yummy!
パカン
Pop
イナゴだけ
Just locusts.
おいしゅうございました♥
It was delicious.
死んじゃえ委員会
The You're Dead Committee
む……
Aaargh!
むきゃ——っ
D-DAMN YOU!
ゆるせまセン!!
Unfor-givable!
殺しマス!!
I'll kill 'em!

食べ物が
絡んだとたん
She changes character
when food's involved.
人格変わってるよ……
吊(つ)るしマス——!!
I'll lynch 'em!
むきー
Furious
Click
スー…
Zzzz

Caught you.
捕まえたぞ
You bastard!
コノヤロ！
Mine!
がぼ!!（確保!!）
Take this wig off!
カツラを取れ!!
Yank
グイッ
Ouch!
痛ぁ〜〜〜い!!
That's my real hair! My own hair!
自毛(じげ)よ自毛!!
STOP!
やめてぇ〜〜〜〜〜〜!!
キャ〜〜っ
Surrender peacefully!
コラッ　おとなしく観念しろ！
STOP!
Aaargh!
いやぁ——!!
You tricked me!
だましたわねぇ
Who the hell are you?
どこのどいつだ!?

おまえは……
You're
the timpanist, Masumi.
ティンパニーの"真澄ちゃん"!?
Yikes!
げっ
Is he your friend, Ryutaro?
峰(みね)くんの友達!?
No, um...
いや……つか
I took classes in
wind and strings with him.
管弦学科の同級生で ずっと授業がいっしょだったから……
Let go!
放してよ!!
Mr Stayed-Back-a-Year!
留年太郎(たろう)!
My name is Ryutaro.
龍太郎(りゅうたろう)だ!!
Why do you play practical jokes on me? What is the You're Dead Committee?
なんでわたしにイタズラするんですか!? 死んじゃえ委員会ってなんですか!?
Don't all shout at me. I'm getting a headache.
みんなで 怒鳴(どな)らないでよ あたま痛いじゃないのよ! なんなのよ!!
Scream, screech
キーー
キィーッ

とにかくアンタ野田恵!
You, Megumi Noda!
千秋さまに近づかないで!
Leave Shinichi Chiaki alone!
いっ……
Er...
はぁ〜〜〜…… なんだ
Oh. I see.
そーゆーことか
That's what it was all about.
そ……
All about? What?
そーゆーことって どーゆーことでスカ!? なんで千秋先輩……?
Why's he going on about Chiaki?
千秋さまはわたしの王子様……
Chiaki is my prince charming.
遠くから見つめるだけで 生きる勇気と希望を与えてくださる わたしのアポロン♡
My Apollo. Just looking at him from a distance gives me the strength to go on.
つまり太陽
The sun around which all revolves.
アポロン千秋
Chiaki/Apollo

Thrust
Then you come along.
This mess of a woman!
It's astonishing that Chiaki would do so much for you.
Can you make copies?
ギャ～
Oooh!
キィ～
Seething
Just 'cos you live next door doesn't give you the right to be so pushy.
毎日毎日ごはん作ってもらったりしてっ
Having him cook for you day after day.
Wow! You're up to date.
A shrimp like you? Never!
You're totally unsuitable for Chiaki.
At least Saiko Tagaya is in his league.
ハァ
Pant, pant
ハァ
Shrimp...
Um...
Chiaki is a guy.
SO WHAT?
He's gay.
Problem with that?

それがなに!? 最近視界に入ってくる このこ汚い女はっ

なんで 千秋さまとあんなことやこんなこと…… 信じらんない!!

焼き増しお願いしマス!!

家がとなりだからって 図々(ずうずう)しいのよ!!

よく調べてあるじゃねーか……

許せない! こんなチンチクリン 千秋さまの背景にふさわしくないのよ

これだったら多賀谷彩子(たがやさいこ)のほうがずっとマシよ!!

チンチクリン…

あの……

千秋先輩は男ですヨ?

だからなに?

そういうシュミの人だ

悪い!?

こうなったら野田恵！

It's time to settle things. Megumi Noda,

わたしと勝負しなさい！

you have me to contend with.

ぎっ……

Golly!

こうなったらって……どーなったんだよ

Settle what things?

なんでイキナリ勝負……

Contend with what?

勝負…

Contend?

とにかくこいつには負けたくないのよ！

I'm not letting her win.

どっちが女として上か思い知らせてやるわ

I'll show her who's more of a woman.

電波同士の対決か……おもしろそーだな

A contest between two nutters on completely different wavelengths. Hmm, this could be interesting.

ドキ

ドキ

Thump, thump

でも……なにで勝負すンの？

How are you going to settle it?

ティンパニーで

With the timpani.

じゃあわたしはピアノで

Then I'll do it with the piano.

そんな勝負あるか——!!

What kind of contest is that?

もっとわかりやすい勝負にしろよ!
You want something that produces clear results.
なによそれっ
Like what?
そうだな例えば……
OK, well...
千秋とのデートの約束をしたほうが勝ち!とか
The one who gets Chiaki to agree to a Christmas Eve date
2週間後の24日……
two weeks from now is the winner.
3人ともアホでした
All 3 of them are nuts.
For example.
2週間後の
Two weeks from now?
24日……
Dec. 24?
クリスマス・イブ デート勝負!!
THE CHRISTMAS EVE DATE CONTEST IS ON!
見て見て!龍ちゃん
Ryutaro, look!
じゃーーん!
Voila!
インザギ・クリスマス
2001年 12月 24日 開演
18:00 開場 19:00
SS席1階G-24
¥30,0
2222-4568
Inzaghi Christmas Dec. 24, 2001 from 7 p.m.
SS seat, 1F, G-24 ¥30,000
キング・オブ指揮者インザギの来日クリスマス公演のチケット♡
Tickets to maestro Inzaghi's concert on Christmas Eve! He's the king of conductors!

おお——っ
すっげ——！
Wow!
これプレミアもんの
チケットだろ——
This is a gold-plated ticket!
キャ
ふんぱつしちゃった〜〜〜♡ 千秋さま インザキ好きかしら〜〜〜
I splurged! I wonder if Chiaki likes Inzaghi.
Yippety-doo!
好き
好き！
He'll love it.
オーケストラ大好き！
He loves orchestras.
あいつ
こーゆーのに
いちばん
よろめく
タイプだから
This will make his jaw drop.
なんだぁつまんねーな——
もうのだめに
勝ったも同然じゃん！
You've practically won. How boring!
Ha-ha-ha!
でも……
But...
こんなコンサート誘うまえに お友達にならないと……
Before I invite him, I have to become friends with him.
ドキドキドキドキ
Thump, thump, thump
こ……声
かけなきゃ……
I-I have to speak to him.
ああ！ でも
What if he says
わたしなんかと
いっしょに行くの
イヤだって言われたら
どうしよう!!
he doesn't want to go with me?
わたし
死んじゃう!!
死んでしまう
I'll die! Just die!
ヒイイ どうしよー
Yikes!
I'm scared, I'm scared
大丈夫
大丈夫♡
You'll be fine.
オレが千秋と友達になれる とっておきの秘策を教えてやるよ
Here's a secret trick to becoming friends with Chiaki.

はい！
Yes.
24日にふたりでどこかに食事に行きませんか!?
Why don't we go out for a meal together?
はあ～？
Excuse me?
24日？
Christmas Eve?
なんでオレがおまえとどこかへ行かなきゃいけないんだ
Why should I go out somewhere with you?
だから食事に……
Just a meal...
いつも食ってるだろう
We're always eating together.
いやその……たまには外で食べるのもどうかと……
I just thought it would be nice to eat out for a change.
ん～～～♬
Humm mm...
!?
ん～～♬
Hum...
ここのチェロはヴィオラと混ぜて……
I'll blend the cello here with the viola...
んん～～♬
Hum mm..
ここでクラリネット！
And the clarinet here.

おう♬
ん？
先輩
ピッチカート
Piccicato
Chiaki...
So cool!
ステキ…♡
Yes?
Yep!
トランペット全開！
Trumpet full blast!
パァー
へー♬
24日……わたし部屋を掃除してケーキ作りマス!!
On Christmas Eve I'll clean my room and bake a cake.
Oh-la.
だから先輩　うちに来てください！
So please come to my place.
むきゃー
やったぁ――♡
Yippee!
I did it!
もう勝った――！
I've won already!
ね――見て見て
Look, look!
コレ早川（はやかわ）くんじゃな～い？
Isn't this Hayakawa?
あ――っ本当だ！　すご～い
Yes. Wow!
早川くんってドイツに留学した指揮科の――？
Hayakawa? The conducting major who went to study in Germany?
そうそう
U-huh.

An audition-based course, often a gateway to the world of professional conducting.
オーディションで選ばれた若手指揮者の登龍門
ちょっと見せてっ！
早川(ハム)がゲルハルムの受講生!?
あの有名なゲルハルムの公開セミナーの受講生になるなんて　スゴーイ！
Wow! He's going to study at the famous Gerharm Academy!
へー
Splutter
ゴフ
Hayakawa's attending the Gerharm Academy?
Can I see that?
最年少じゃな〜い？
He must be the youngest.
え……あっ
Ooh, er...
はいっ
Yes!
CLASSIC JAPAN
ギャー
千秋さまっ
Chiaki!
キャー
Squeal
そんな……
It can't be true.
特別取材
〜第15回〜
ゲルハルム公開セミナー
Gerharm Academy Holds 15th Seminar
Prof. Vieira also teaches.
ヴィエラ先生も講師を……
だってあのセミナーでは
In that seminar...

ナンダヨソレ……
What's this rubbish?
日本から唯一参加した
早川有紀夫君（22）
ヴィエラから指導を受け
Yukio Hayakawa, 22, the only student from Japan, receives instruction from Prof. Vieira.
〝千秋におまえの華麗なティンパニーを聴かせてやるんだ〟
Let Chiaki see what a brilliant timpanist you are.
Roll
〝千秋に認められれば友達になれる〟
Once he recognizes your talent, he'll be your friend.
Boom-boom
〝オレのようにな！〟
Worked with me.
Boom-bu-bu-boom
今度のオケのリハで　わたしも羽ばたいてみせる!!
I'll be sublime at the next rehearsal.
龍ちゃんのように…
Just like Ryutaro.

のだめ……なにやってんの？
Nodame, what are you doing?
ケーキの練習です
Practicing making cakes.
Rattle, whip
いや……だから
What I mean is
なんで学校でやるのかって……
why are you doing it at school?
Rattle, rattle, whip
クリスマスはもーすぐだから――♡
Because it's almost Christmas.
メレンゲメレンゲ～もた～ん♫
♫Meringue, meringue... Do the merengue, cha-cha-cha.♫
結局……
Ultimately,
R-rrip
こんな勉強ひとりでしてたところで なんになるっていうんだ――
what's the point of studying this all alone?

Lesson 8

こんな曲作ったところで
なんになるっていうんだ――
What's the point of composing such a piece?
いくら勉強しても
早川(ハム)にさえ
負けてるオレ
No matter how hard I study, I can't even keep up with Hayakawa.
ただ飛行機に乗れないだけで 結局は
Just because I'm afraid of flying,
このまま人知れず日本で消えてゆくしかないのか!?
am I doomed to obscurity here in Japan?
また鬱期突入中
Catapulting into depression again.
ピンポーン。。
Ding-dong!

殺すリスト最上位!!

She's at the top of my hit list.

うで組んだ、うで組んだ…うで組んだ

Arm-in-arm!
Arm-in-arm!
Arm-in-arm!

ザッ

Scribble, scribble

ザッ

I guess this is OK.

ふー

Sigh

まあ……こんなもんだろ

すご〜〜〜い！この曲 千秋先輩が作ったんですか〜〜〜!?

ロマンチック——♡

しゅてき——！

ロマン……そうかあ？

第２楽章だからか？

タイトルは〈のだめ♡ラプソディ〉で決まりですね！

決めるな!! 勝手（かって）にっ

この曲はそのうちオケ用に全部書いてみるつもりで……

もう少しハデな曲になる予定なんだ

オーケストラ!!

じゃあ管弦とか全部考えるんですか!?

まあ…な

すご——い!!

曲を作ったところでオケはないが……

学生の分際で当たりまえだけど

千秋せんぱぁ〜い♡
Chiaki!
ぎゃほー♡
Yoo-hoo!
Chocolate flavor
チョコ味
Strawberries
Cream flavor
クリーム味
Ingredients
具
Jam
ジャム
Pizza flavor
ピザ味
Cheese
チーズ
Salami
サラミ
Sponge
スポンジ
Curry flavor
カレー味
Carrots
ニンジン
Curry
カレー
Meat
肉
What kind of Christmas cake
would you like?
クリスマスのケーキ
なに味がいいデスか〜〜〜?
クリスマスって……
Christmas?
What are you talking about?
なにそれ?
え〜〜〜っ クリスマスって わたしと先輩がふたりでケーキをつつく聖なる夜のことですヨ〜〜〜♡
Oh my! The holy night when we eat our cake together!
You promised!
キャ♡
Tee-hee!
約束したじゃないですかー
Don't remember.
知らん
えっ……
What!
You promised you would come to my place on Christmas Eve...
でも……24日はわたしの部屋でクリスマスしようって約束……
Know nothing about it.
知るか! そんな約束
あう…
Oh...
Why on earth should I spend Christmas with you?
なんでオレがおまえとクリスマスなんか!

I'm busy now.
オレは今忙しいんだっ
Don't drop by with all sorts of silly excuses.
くだらない用事で いちいちうちに来るな！
Leave me alone!
ほっといてくれ!!
And eat dinner by yourself!
メシも自分で食えっ
Slam
Oh dear...
ガーーン……
Christmas?
なにがクリスマスだ
How idiotic!
バカバカしい！

アホな人間とつきあってると　よけい落ち込む
I get even more depressed when I hang out with idiots.
千秋ィー
CHIAKI!
どうして……
This can't be happening.
チャオー
Ciao!
千秋！ 今日 これから ヒマー？
Hey, are you free today?
また天然のアホが来る!? ヒマじゃねえ！
Another born idiot.
よるなっ
No, I'm not free.
Go away!
スタ
Rush, hurry
スタ
え～～ 授業終わったんだろ？
Why? You've finished class, haven't you?
これからホールで Aオケの練習 あるらしーから 見にいかねえ!?
I'm going to an Orchestra A rehearsal. Wanna come?
オレの友達が ティンパニー やってンだよ♡
My buddy's the timpanist.

行かん！
I'll pass.
なんで
——!?
Why?
峰の友達……
Ryutaro's buddy?
アホにきまってる
Bound to be an idiot.
すっごい
うまいんだぜ
そいつー
He's brilliant.
絶対
聴(き)いてみる
価値あるからー
He's definitely worth hearing.
いやだっ
No.
将来有望の
天才ティンパニー奏者！
A genius timpanist with a great future!
まぁ だまされたと思ってー
Come on, you've got nothing to lose.
あはは…
Shrieks of laughter
I don't believe it.
うそォー
どーしたの？そのカッコ
Why are you dressed like that?
何ごと～？
What on earth...?
あはは
Ha-ha-ha!
やだーっ真澄ちゃん 本番じゃあるまいし
Masumi, it's just a rehearsal.

わたしは
今日の練習に
命かけてンのよ
My life depends on today's rehearsal.
あんたたち
絶対ヘマ
すんじゃないわよ!!
I'm counting on you girls not to screw up.
キィ〜〜
Scowl, lecture
え〜〜っ
What?
なんで〜〜?
Why?
練習なのに〜
It's just a rehearsal.
だって
Because
なんで正装ー?
Why a tux?
うるさいわね!
Shut up!
悪い!?
Any complaints?
だって今日は……
Because today...

千秋さま♡
Chiaki!
きてくれた～!!
He came!
今日ハ
第2楽章カラ
ハジメマス
デハ
OK.
Today we're starting with the 2nd movement.
外国人先生
Prof. is foreigner
コンコン
Tap, tap
ベートーヴェン交響曲第9番第2楽章――
Beethoven's Symphony No. 9, the 2nd movement.
見ててください千秋さま♡
Please watch me, most adored Chiaki.
奥山(おくやま)真澄(21)
Masumi Okuyama, 21.
あなたへの熱い想(おも)いを このティンパニーに託します――
I will channel all my passion for you in this timpani.

聴いて！
わたしの
この想い

ドドンドド
オーン
BONGA-BONGA-BOOM!
be my friend.
友達になってください♡
Shake, tremble
わな
わな…
Stop,
stop!
ストップ!
ストープッ
Timpani!
GET OUT!
ティンパニー
出てけー!!
What?
えっ

えっ……

Sorry?
Clank
That's your buddy?
Ryutaro?
Um, well, er...
あわわ…
Dear, oh dear
He's a total buffoon.

あれがおまえの友達か

峰

いや……っ
あれは……

最悪の
アホだな

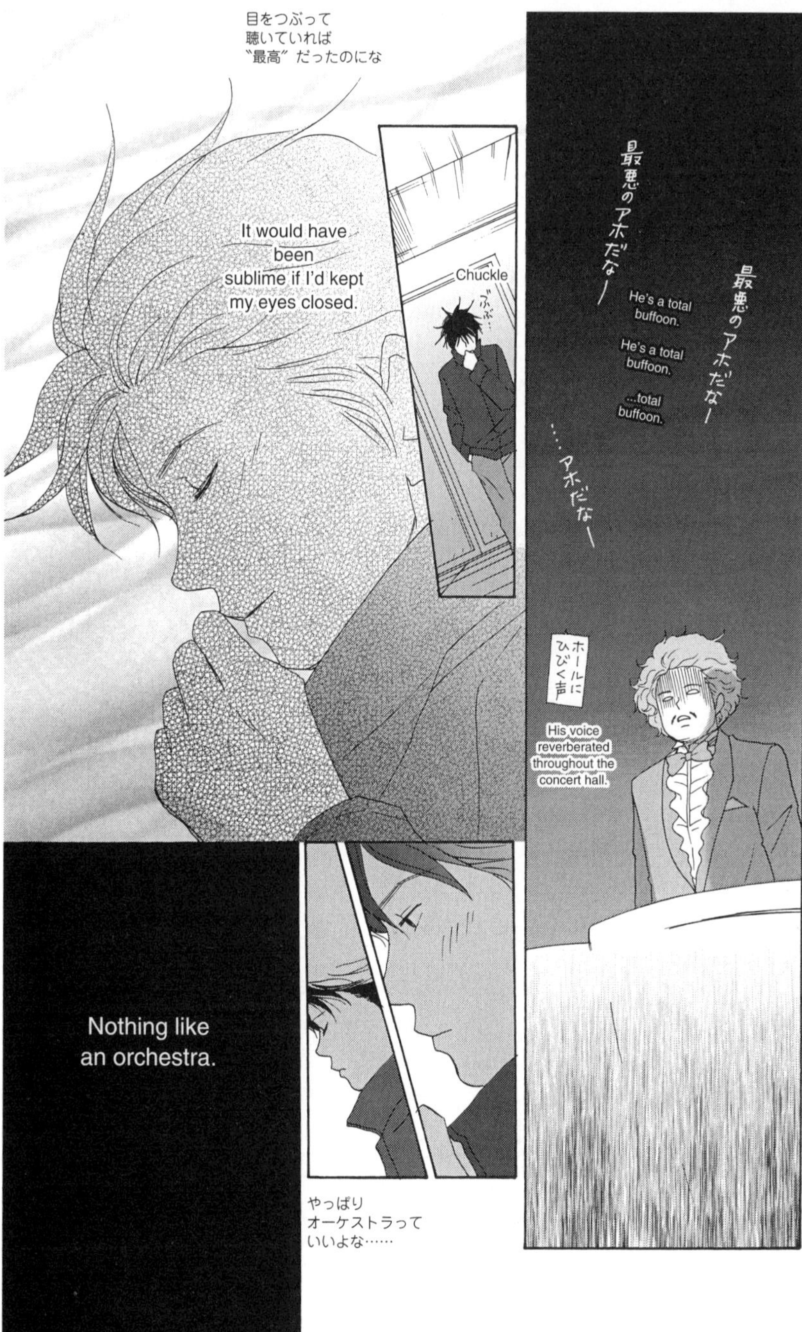
最悪のアホだなー
最悪のアホだなー
He's a total buffoon.
He's a total buffoon.
…アホだなー
...total buffoon.
目をつぶって
聴いていれば
"最高"だったのにな
It would have been sublime if I'd kept my eyes closed.
ぷぷ…
Chuckle
ホールにひびく声
His voice reverberated throughout the concert hall.
やっぱり
オーケストラって
いいよな……
Nothing like an orchestra.

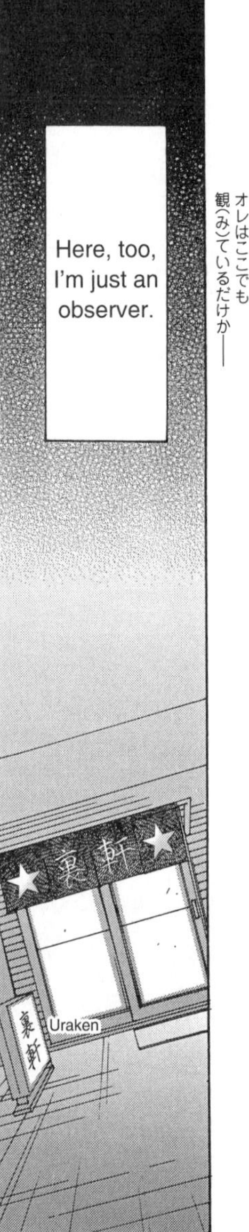

オレはここでも観(み)ているだけか——

Clink

Vegetable fried rice
Pork cutlet fried rice
Kimchi fried rice
We now do burgers
Uraken rice bowl

My condolences,

both of you.

ご愁傷(しゅうしょう)さまでした

ふたりとも

Sob

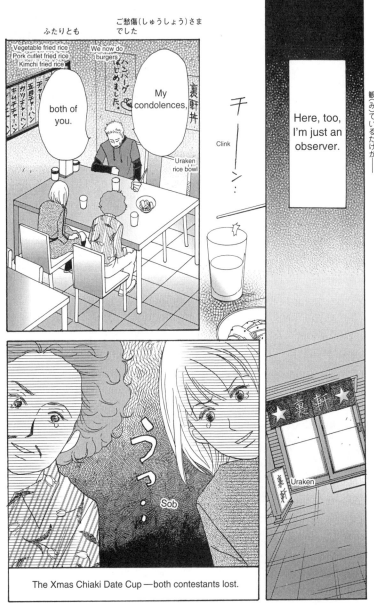

The Xmas Chiaki Date Cup—both contestants lost.

〝クリスマス♡千秋とデート杯〟—— 両者敗退

わーっ
Why did he suddenly change his mind?
Why was I kicked out of the concert hall?
Bawl
He promised!
All I did was express my love!
Maybe he didn't go for a pizza flavor cake.
It's his fault! That prof. who was conducting!
It was all wrong, wasn't it?
Don't drop by.... Leave me alone!
I don't know what to do.
ぶひゃ
Weep
I have no home, no-one to love.
You at least have hope.
A total buffoon
He'll never be my friend. He now holds *me* in complete contempt!
あるだろ…家
You do have a home.
どーしてわたしが
退場させられる
のよ——!!
愛を表現
しただけ
なのに！
ピザ味の
ケーキが
いけなかったん
でしょーか!?
あの指揮の
先生がいけな
かったのよね!?
どーして先輩は急に態度をひるがえしたんでしょうかぁ　約束したのに！
なにもかもが
いけなかったん
だろ……
来るな！　ほっといてくれ！　のだめ　これからどうしたら……　帰る家も愛もなくして……
あんたなんか
まだマシよ！
わたしなんか……
最悪の
アホだな
友達になるどころか
人として激しく軽蔑（けいべつ）
されちゃったのよ！

まったく……真澄ちゃん普通に叩(たた)いてればよかったのに

踊るティンパニー奏者なんて見たことねーよバカじゃねーの

峰くんも よく踊ってますヨ?

どうしたらいいのわたし……

オケまでクビにされちゃって

ティンパニーをひとりで叩くなんて…… 耐えられない!

もうお終(しま)いだわ!!

もう山形に帰るしかないんだわ——!!

そ……そこまで思いつめなくても

あんたたちはいいわよね

もともと落ちこぼれだし

ヴァイオリンにピアノ——

どっちもひとりで演奏できる楽器だものね……

both instruments you can play on your own.

わたしはひとりじゃ輝けない

I can't play on my own.

真澄ちゃん……

Masumi...

あの……

Um...

What?

3人でアンサンブルやってみませんか？

Why don't the three of us play **ensemble**?

ピアノとヴァイオリンとティンパニーで

Piano, violin and timpani.

真一(しんいち) 今年のクリスマスはどうしてる?
Shinichi,
what are you doing for Christmas?
またクリスマスの話か……
Christmas again.
どうって別に……
Nothing special.
ふ〜ん… やっぱりねぇ〜
I knew it.
また今年もうちでパーティーあるらしいけど来る?
It seems my folks are having a party again. Would you like to come?
それとも今年はふたりっきりで過ごす?
Or would you like to spend it just the two of us?
真一の部屋でわたしケーキとか焼いちゃおっかなー♡
Maybe I'll come to your place and bake a cake.
24日……わたし部屋を掃除してケーキ作りマス!! あ……
On Christmas Eve I'll clean up and bake a cake.
Oh!
だから先輩うちに来てくだサイ!
So please come to my place.
おう♪
Hey,
思い出した……
I remember.
真一?
Shinichi?
聞いてる!?
Are you listening to me?

約束は約束だからな……
彩子……悪いけど
Sorry Saiko, I have to go.
Pizza flavor
ピザ味
Curry flavor
カレー味
201
野田
201 NODA
ピンポーン
Ding-dong
べつに義理立てする理由はないが――
Not like I have an obligation.
But a promise is a promise.
"味"って……?
Flavor?
ちゃんと丁寧(ていねい)にお断りしよう!
It's only polite
to say no properly.
ピンポン
Ding-dong
なんだ留守(るす)か
Oh, she's out.
シーン
Silent
最近のだめ見なくない?
Have any of you seen Nodame? I haven't.
まあいいか
Doesn't matter.
Hey, you guys!
どうせすぐうちに来るだろ……
Bet she'll be round to my place soon.
3日間ほど!
Not for 3 days.
ねーねー

あー……
そういえば
いないよね
Come to think of it, I haven't.
いつも昼ごはんにはいるのに…
She always shows up for lunch.
授業には
出てるみたい
だけどー
I hear she does show up for class.
どこでなに
やってンのかなー
What's she up to?
あんなにまとわりついてきてたのに
She used to follow me like a lapdog.
とうとうのだめにまで忘れられたか　オレ
Even Nodame has forgotten me.
世界は　あっというまに変わってゆく……
Things change
in the blink of an eye.

え？

ちょっとなによ！あんたのそのリズム!!

この曲……!?

Why do you suddenly change tempo when I'm beating at 120?
わたしが120で叩いてンのに なんで途中から テンポ変えるのよ!!
Stop it. It's creepy!
気持ち悪いじゃないの!!
走ってンのよっ
You're galloping ahead.
タメるのはいいけど 走んないでよね の駄目!
Saving it is fine but don't gallop ahead, Noddy-No-Brains.
フンッ
Huh!
え〜〜っ そんなリズム 狂ってますか〜〜?
Is the rhythm that off?
わからナ〜イ
I didn't hear it.
真澄ちゃんの リズムが正確 すぎるんだよー
Masumi, you're rhythm is too precise.
人間メトロノーム…
The human metronome.
のだめデスー!!
It's NODAME!
ムキー
Seethe
まあまあ
OK, OK.
じゃあ もう一回頭からー
Once more, from the top.
We're playing jazz. So be a bit more flexible. Play around a bit, drop the tempo, save a bit of something there.
ジャズなんだから そのへんもう少しラフにやろーよ タメとか大事だしー
ドラムセット
Drum set.

オレの
作った曲——
It's my
piece.
あいつ 一回しか聴いてないのに
She's got it,
even though
she's
only heard it
once.
They've
rearranged
it as jazz.
みんなでジャズに
アレンジして——

いい曲よねーコレ♡
Such a lovely piece!
さすが千秋さまの作った曲……♡
Only to be expected from the divine Chiaki!
幸せ…♡
Ooh, bliss!
OF COURSE IT IS!
当然だ——
でもな～
Still,
やっぱベースいないの無理があるよなー
it needs a bass.
ジャズだしィ
After all, it's jazz.
IT WASN'T MEANT FOR JAZZ!
アレンジにだって無理がある
のだめの腕がもう一本あったら～～～
If I had another arm,
ピアノでベースやれるのにィ
I could play bass too!
…………

腕一本でよかったら
Need an arm?
Here it is.
参加するけど——?

な……なんだよ　その反応
W-What's wrong?
カ
Flush
悪いか!?
Any complaints?
No point wallowing in envy.
他人(ひと)の世界をうらやんでいても仕方ない

Dec. 24
Christmas Eve.

そして学校
At school
ヒュウウウ
Whooosh

We are each responsible for changing our own reality.
自分の世界は　自分で変えなければ——
わーっ
Yikes!
真澄ちゃんが失神したーっ
Oh no! Masumi's fainted!
ほげーっ
Golly!

のだめは今のとこ
もうちょっと抑え気味で
ヴァイオリンを前に出して
Nodame, hold back a bit and let the violin come out more.
峰はソロ入る前のフレーズ突っ込みすぎ
Ryutaro, you are too aggressive in that phrase before the solo.
モジャモジャは
36小節目のフィル
2拍前から入って
Frizzball, come in two beats before the 36th note.
じゃあ
今のトコ
直して
So, fix those bits
もう一回
最初から
and once again, from the top.
な……なんだよ　その反応
W-What's wrong?
なにか
文句あるのか？
Any complaints?

いい加減にしろよ!!
Is there no pleasing you?
何日やれば気が済むんだよ
How long do you plan to keep us at it?
細かすぎるんだよ!!
You're too fastidious!
"モジャモジャ"って呼ぶのはやめて——!!
Please stop calling me Frizzball!
Weep
真澄って呼んで——
Please call me Masumi!
今日はクリスマスパーティーするって言ったくせに——!!
We agreed to have a Christmas party today!
Bawl!
ケーキ
Cake!
かつどん~~~!!
Pork cutlets on rice!
だったら さっさと完璧(かんぺき)に演(や)れ——!!
Then hurry up and get it right!
ぎゃぼ——
Aaargh!
こうして4人の初アンサンブルは
Due to Chiaki's perfectionism,
千秋の完璧主義の前に年内に終わることがなかった
the new quartet showed no signs of closing shop at the end of the year.
裏軒
Uraken

Lesson 9

室町時代に登場し　現代に至るまで
日本人に愛され続けている
冬の暖房器具　　　　　　　　　　こたつ――――

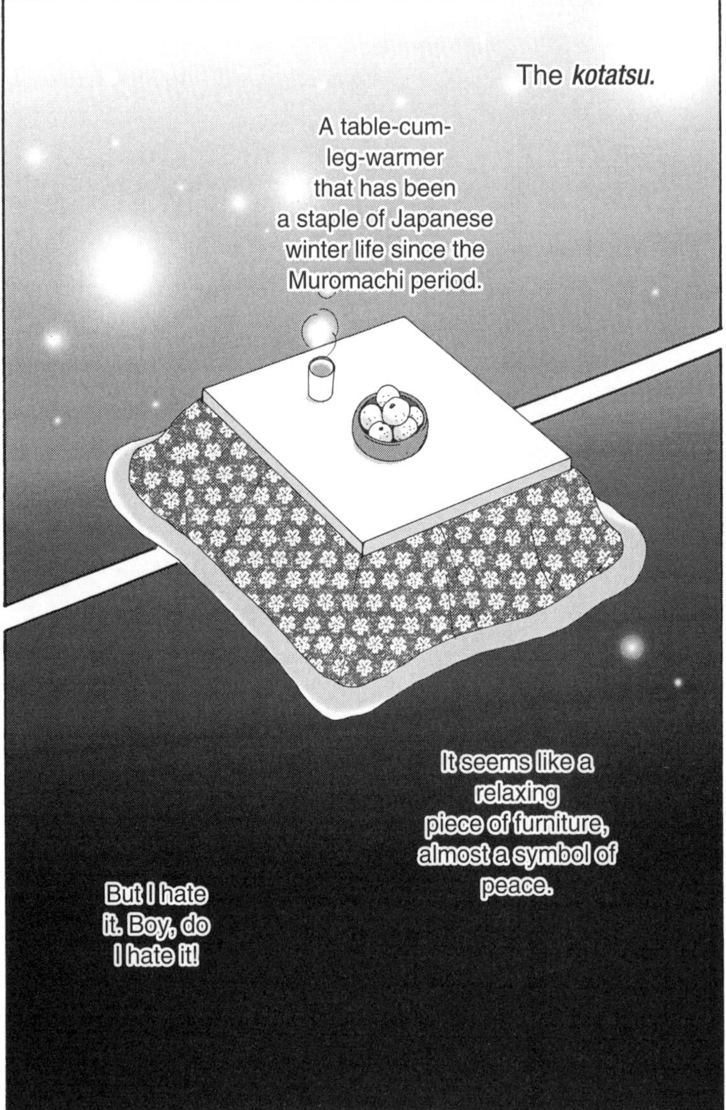

The *kotatsu.*
A table-cum-leg-warmer that has been a staple of Japanese winter life since the Muromachi period.
It seems like a relaxing piece of furniture, almost a symbol of peace.
But I hate it. Boy, do I hate it!

しかし　こんなにのんきで攻撃性のない
平和の象徴のような物体が……

オレは今
憎くて憎くて
仕方がない――

はじまりは去年の年末――

It all started at the end of last year.

You're not going back to your folks?

え……おまえ実家に帰らないの？

No. You said you weren't going home either.

ハイ！ 千秋先輩も帰らないっていうし

It's a great chance.

絶好のチャンスですから♡

Chance for what?

なんのチャンスだ!?

Love, of course!

恋の……

キャ♡ Squeal

Go home, go home!

帰れ帰れ!!

星へ帰れーっ

Back to your planet!

Now, now!

Let's cook a *nabe* stew together.

まあまあそう言わずに ふたりで鍋をやりましょう♡

A *nabe*?

鍋え〜〜〜!?

Yes, my folks sent me a *nabe* kit.

実家から鍋セットが届いたんデス！

PLONK

痩身茶

Dietetic tea

野菜と肉ー

Vegetables and meat

おまえが
台無しに
したんだろ……
このあいだの鍋は
イナゴが台無(だいな)しに
しちゃったんで再挑戦ですね♡
You made a hash of it.
We made a hash of it last time thanks to the locusts. So let's try again.
こんぶ～♫
konbu kelp
むいいしいたけ！
Great shiitake mushrooms!
なに？　どうかした？
What's wrong?
ん～～……
Hmm...
先輩の部屋とってもキレイなんだけどなにかがたりない……
Your place is great. But it lacks something.
オレはなるべく物を置かない主義なんだ　なんか文句あるか？
I make a point of avoiding clutter.
Problem with that?
はぁ～～？
Excuse me?
あっ
Oh!
そか!!
I know!

ドン
DUMP

This!
A *kotatsu.*

これこれ！ こたつ！

A *nabe* is not a *nabe* without one.

鍋にはやっぱりこたつでしょう♡

What the...

な……

Do not bring that thing in here.

そんなもん うちに持ちこむな――!!

え
What!

Why not?

いけませんか？

It's obvious.

あたりまえだ!!

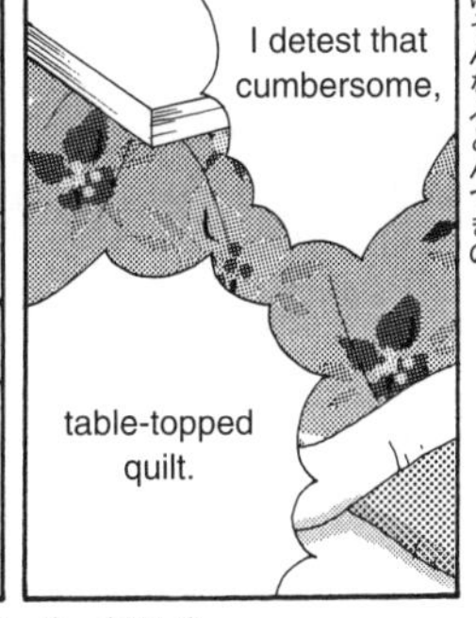

オレはそんなふとんつきの
もっさりした
テーブルは
大キライなんだ!!

大キライって
そんな~~~

こーんな
気持ちのいい物
この世にふたつと
ないじゃないですかー

先輩だって
入ったことぐらい
あるでしょ~~~!?

じつは――
オレは生まれてから一度もこたつに入ったことがなかった
Actually, I haven't.
Not once.
小さいころは海外で生活
When I was small I lived abroad.
ヨーロッパ
Europe
日本では母の実家が洋式の家で
Once back in Japan, I lived with my mother's parents in a Western-style house.
畳の部屋さえ一室もなかった
There wasn't a single, Japanese-style room.
友人の家やＴＶではよく見たこたつ……
I'd seen *kotatsu* in friends' houses and on TV.
ぐつ
Bubble
ぐつ
Simmer
もうお肉入れてもいいですかね〜〜〜
Time to put the meat in now?
……
ちょん…
Settle
これがこたつ……
So this is *kotatsu* life.
じんわりぬく
Warm and cosy

あったかい……
Warm as toast.
先輩！もう野菜も煮えてますよ～
The vegetables are ready!
ぐつぐつ
Bubble, simmer
のだめ妻だから取ってあげマス♡
I'll do my wifely duty and serve you!
だれが妻だ…
What wifely duty?
まぁいいか
I guess it's OK
ほのぼの～
Cosy
はいあなた♥
Here darling.
一日くらいこたつ体験……
to have a day in a *kotatsu.*
チュン
チュン…
Chirp-chirp
Mmm?
ん……

ぶごっ
Snore
げっ
Yikes!
しまった〰〰
昨日食いすぎて　つい……
Darn! I overate last night and fell asleep
こたつで
そのまま
in the *kotatsu.*
ほがー
Zzzz
ピアノの
練習も
忘れて……
I forgot about piano practice.
まぁ
いいか……
I guess it's OK.
鍋の片づけもピアノの練習も
もうひと眠りしてからで
I'll have another snooze before I clean up and practice the piano.
ぬくぬく〜
Comfy and cosy
こたつって　なかなか出がたい――
It's very hard to get out of a *kotatsu.*

「新婚さんこんにちは♡」
Hi there, newlyweds!
ラブラブ年忘れスペシャル♡♡♡
It's a lovely-dovey year-end special!
いらっしゃい
Hi there!
Cheers, applause
いいなー♡ 新婚さん
Must be nice to be newly wed.
ラブラブ
Lovey-dovey
のだめも出た〜〜い♡
I want to be on this show too!
あ!
Hey!
先輩 こんばんは〜〜
Good evening!
ツヤなし 無造作ヘアですねー♡
You've got the tousled, natural look!
ぎゃぴ
Tee-hee!

さっき部屋に帰ったら
ちょうど実家から
ミカンが届いたんですヨ～～
どーん
Dump
I popped back to my place and found a delivery of mandarin oranges from my family!
みかん
先輩も
おひとつ
いかがですか?
Can I offer you one?
のだめ
妻だから
むいてあげマス♡
I'll peel it for you—after all, I'm your wife.
ちょっと
まて……
Hang on.
なんで おまえ
パジャマでうちに？
Why are you here in your pyjamas?
ドキー
Oh!
それになんだ？ あのTVは
And the TV!
なんでソファーの上に!?
Why is it on the sofa?
だって——
先輩のうち
TVを床に
置いてて
Well, if it's on the floor,
おこたが
高くて
見えないしィ
it's hard to see from the *kotatsu.*
なら自分の部屋で見ろよ！
Then watch TV in your own place!
のだめの部屋おこたがないと寒くて——
But it's so cold without the *kotatsu.*
みかん みかん

だったら
もう持って
帰れ！

Then take it home!

ここに
住みつくん
じゃねぇ!!

Don't squat here!

まぁ
まぁ

Calm down,

あとで
ちゃんと
帰りますから

I'll go home eventually.

とりあえず
ビールなんか
どうですか？

Now, how about a beer?

カン

Clank

先輩おこたで寝たから ノドとか渇いたでしょー

You must be thirsty after dozing in the *kotatsu.*

さっきコンビニで買ってきましたー♡

I popped over to the convenience store and got some.

BEER LAGER

ごくー

Gulp

き……気がきくじゃねーか

H-How thoughtful!

そだっ お鍋！

As for the *nabe,*

材料がまだたくさん残ってるんですヨー

we still have a lot of ingredients left.

負けた

She rules the roost.

ガチャ ガチャ

Rattle, clatter

プシュー

Pop

またお鍋
しましょう♡

So let's have it again.

ぐつ ぐつ

Bubble, simmer

まあ
いいか……

Guess it's OK.

カー

Guzzle

妻だから
とる…♡

I'm your wife, so I'll serve you.

今年ももうすぐ終わりだし(意味なし)
Anyway, this year's almost over.
はい先輩あーーん♡
Come on darling, open!
自分で食う!
I'll eat it myself!
えーー夫のくせにー
Oh hubby!
う…
W-
二日酔(ふつかよ)い……
Hangover...
ガン
ガン
Pound, pound
な……
W-
ごわー
Scary
みかん
Mandarin oranges
なんだこれは!?
What happened here?
まるで　のだめの部屋……
It's like Nodame's room.
の……のだめ!?
Nodame!
帰ったのか
Gone home?
助かった……
Oh good!
ふう…
Sigh
ぐったり…
Drained

とりあえず片づけはあとにして
I'll clean up later.
よれ
Crumpled and stale
風呂（ふろ）……
Need a bath.
のだめ菌を落とさねば……
ザザァ
Gush, splash
I have to get rid of bacillus Nodames.
ザァァ
Pour, scrub
Bath Salts The Hotsprings Collection
日本の名湯
あいつ……
She didn't
うちの風呂に入ったのか!?
take a bath here, did she?
のだめ〰〰
Nodame...
バキィ
Snap
ここに住まわれてたまるか!!
No way is she moving in!

とりあえず一度ちゃんとベッドで寝て　生活を元に戻そう……
I just need to sleep properly in a bed and get things back to normal.
こたつはあとで
叩(たた)き返(かえ)すとして
ガチャンッ
SLAM
玄関ロック！
Door locked
I'll shove the *kotatsu* back in her face later.
ガチャ…
Click
寝室→
Bedroom
スピー
Zzzz
ふ……
Are you
ふざけんな――!!
out of your mind?

宅配便
でーす！

だれだ!?

くそっ

なんちて——　メリーおおみそか——!!

こんばんはー♡

元旦イヴ!!

なんちてー

大ショック

年越しチャーハン
持ってきたぞー！

これ食って
みんなで仲よく
年を越そうぜー！

わたしは
お酒を……♡

千秋さま　お酒が
お好きだって
いうから♡

ふおお——っ
Yikes!
ビックリしたぁ〜〜
You scared me.
どうしたんですか? 先輩
What's up?
どうしたじゃねぇ!!
I'll *what's up*? you!
なんでおまえがオレのベッドで寝てンだ!?
Why are you sleeping in my bed?
勝手(かって)に風呂にまで入りやがって 警察につき出すぞ!
And who said you could take a bath?
I'll hand you over to the police!
キャ
Aaargh!
出ろっ
Get out!
だって〜〜 先輩の部屋お風呂も広いし
Well, you've got such a big and lovely bath!
寝室だってあるしィ
And a proper bedroom!
のだめも久しぶりにベッドで寝てみたかったんデス〜〜
I wanted to sleep in a bed for a change.
おまえのベッドはゴミに埋まってるだけだろ!
You've got a bed! It's just buried under rubbish.
掘り起こせ!!
Excavate it!
わーん
Bawl
ムリですー
I can't
ピンポーン
Ding-dong
あ お客さん
S-Someone is here!

のだめも電話で呼び出すかー？
Let's call Nodame.
ズカ ズカ
Stomp, stride
おじゃまします〰♡
Oh my goodness, don't mind if I do!
キャーキャー
Squeal, squeal
初 千秋さまの部屋〜♡
Ooh, a maiden voyage to a hallowed place!
Uraken
裏軒
あれ〰
Oh!
峰くんに真澄ちゃん？
Ryutaro and Masumi?
いらっ、しゃーい
Nice to see you!
げっ
Jesus!
どーして あんたがここにいるのよ!?
Why the hell are you here?
なにしてんのよッ
What are you up to?
なんでパジャマなのよ!!
Why the pyjamas?
のだめのこたつ……
Nodame's *kotatsu.*
のだめのゴミ……
Nodame's rubbish.

千秋
同棲(どうせい)……
You're living together?
してねえ!!
No!
寄生だ!!
She squatted here!
いいじゃんコレ～♡ 雰囲気あってー
Ha-ha-ha
This is really great.
みんなでぬくぬくしよーぜー
Let's all get cosy together.
こたつこたつ！
Goody! A *kotatsu.*
Uraken
あっ
Eeek!
Pull
もうすぐ紅白はじまりマス！
The Men vs. Women Song Contest is on soon!
きーーっ 殺す!!
この座敷(ざしき)童子(わらし)ー！
I'll kill you!
You cat!
Eeek!
まぁー なんかしんないけど みんなそろったし ちょうどよかった
Come on, we're all here. Might as well celebrate.
キャー!! ダ・パンプ 見なきゃ～～♡
Ooh! Gotta see my favorite boy band, Da Pump.
GOSH!
モー娘。モー娘。♡
I want my fave girl band, Morning Musume.
もうすぐN響の "第九" があるのに……
I was actually looking forward to the NHK Symphony doing Beethoven's 9th.

How did this happen?
どうしてこんなことに!?
Ha, ha, ha!
わははは!!
Golly gosh!
キャ――♡
Yikes!
ぴぎゃ――っ
Wow, look at that costume!
すげー衣装ー
Um, where's the human being?
つか人間どこよ？
Can't sing, as usual.
あいかわらず歌ヘタね〜〜〜この人
Is the Honorable Mr. Maekawa on soon?
前川(まえかわ)先生はまだですか？
Who's the Honorable Mr. Maekawa?
だれよ？ 前川先生って
Kiyoshi Maekawa.
前川きよし♡
Why's he honorable?
なんで"先生"なのよ!!
Where's the TV magazine?
おい TV雑誌どこ――？
Got it, got it.
あ――ありますあります
Mandarin oranges
みかん

ズズー
Drag
ひょい
Here we go.
ポコッ
Toss
Missed
失敗
ねえ　おつまみ　もうないわよ〜〜
We're out of nibbles.
のだめ——っ 酒くれ！ 酒——っ
Nodame, gimme some sake!
のだめ 買ってきてよ
Nodame, go and buy some.
えー
Don't wanna.
やだー さむいー
It's cold.
峰くん 行ってきてヨ
Ryutaro, you go.

オレ今だめー
Can't. I think
ネコが足の上乗ってンだよ
there's a cat on my legs.
どこにネコがいるのよ!!
What cat?
キィー
Whine
うそつきずるいー
Liar, cheat!
そうか……
I see.
今やっとわかった……
I get it now.
諸悪の根元は
The root of all evil
すべてこのこたつだ
is this *kotatsu.*

The *kotatsu* allowed the Nodame invasion.
Its very warmth and cosiness dulls body and mind.
At this rate, they'll be sleeping over. No need for guest mattresses.
Look.
I'll give you some money. So all of you, go and get some booze and snacks. OK?
Slam
Now's my chance.

このこたつとともに　のだめの侵略を許し　このままでは客用のふとんなどないオレのうちでも　こいつらを容易に泊めてしまえるだろう――

このぬくぬくとした温度とふとんで　身体(からだ)と頭の感覚を鈍らせ　人間を脱力させる

おい

金はやるから　みんなでコンビニ行って　酒とつまみ買ってこい！

今のうちだ

Unlock
I found a fantastic *kotatsu* outside!
Look, look!
Now we can **each** have one.
Large rubbish
粗大ゴミ
No, please!
I can't take this anymore!
What?
Chiaki realized that his adversary had always been Nodame, not the *kotatsu.*

今外ですんごーい　いいこたつ拾っちゃった〰〰！　これで一家に一台置けますヨ〰〰♡

敵は最初から
こたつではなく
「のだめ」だったのだと
悟った千秋だった――

はぁー？

**頼むから
もうやめて
くれ――!!**

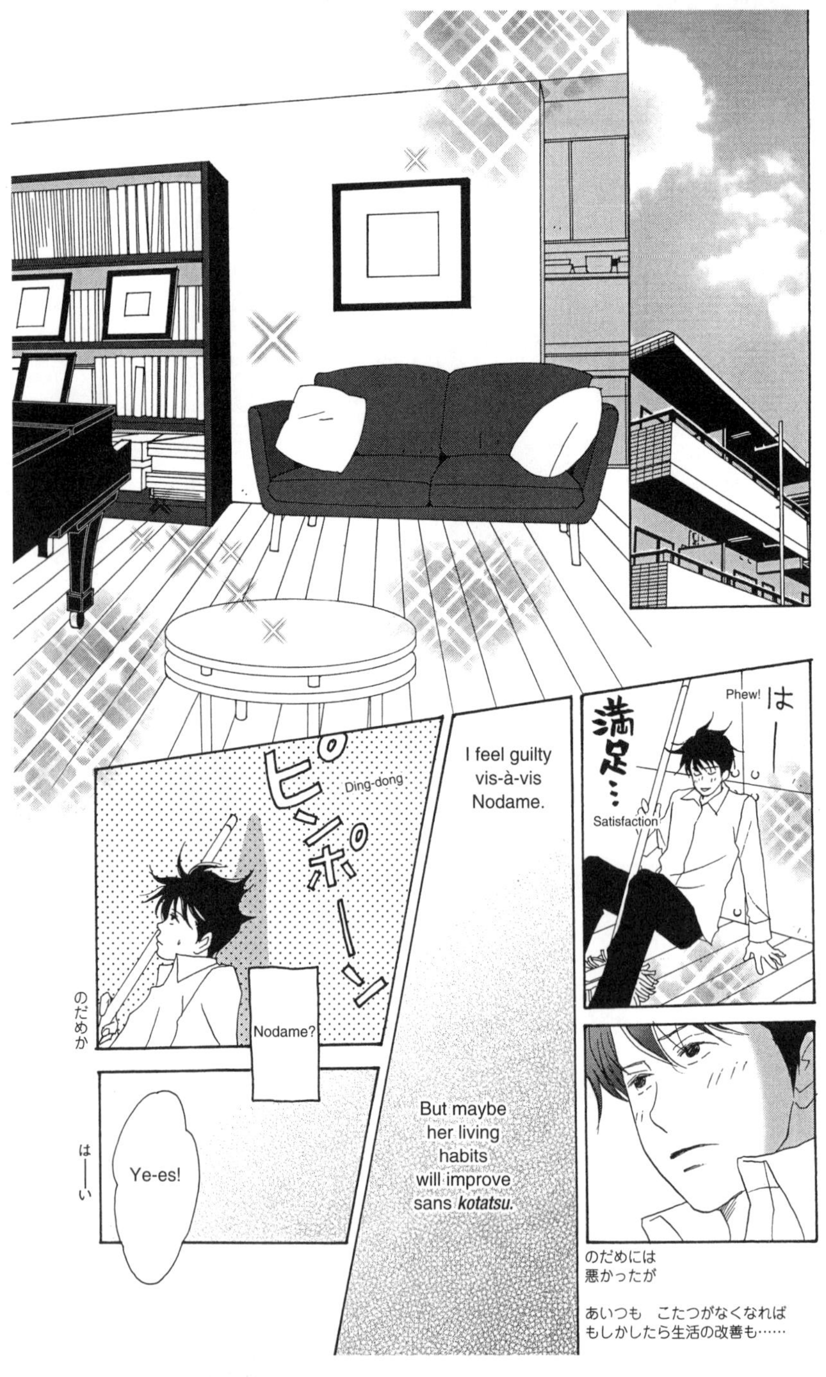
満足……
Satisfaction
はー
Phew!
I feel guilty vis-à-vis Nodame.
のだめには
悪かったが
あいつも　こたつがなくなれば
もしかしたら生活の改善も……
But maybe her living habits will improve sans *kotatsu.*
ピンポーン
Ding-dong
のだめか
Nodame?
は——い
Ye-es!

バイリンガル版 のだめカンタービレ ①

Nodame Cantabile ①

2007年3月28日　第1刷発行
2015年3月25日　第15刷発行

著　者　　二ノ宮知子

訳　者　　玉置百合子

発行者　　鈴木 哲

発行所　　株式会社講談社

〒112-8001　東京都文京区音羽2-12-21

販売部　東京03-5395-3622

業務部　東京03-5395-3615

編　集　　株式会社講談社エディトリアル

代表　田村 仁

〒112-0013　東京都文京区音羽1-17-18　護国寺SIAビル

編集部　東京03-5319-2171

本文印刷　豊国印刷株式会社

カバー印刷・製本　大日本印刷株式会社

定価はカバーに表示してあります。　　　　編集協力　武蔵エディトリアル

Printed in Japan

ISBN978-4-7700-4072-5

のだめ
カンタービレ

Nodame
Cantabile